MOMENTS IN LEADERSHIP

CASE STUDIES IN
PUBLIC HEALTH POLICY
AND PRACTICE

Editors

Barbara DeBuono, MD, MPH

Executive Director
Public Health
and Government
Pfizer Inc

Ana Rita Gonzalez, ScD

Senior Vice President
and Partner
Fleishman-Hillard
International Communications

Sara Rosenbaum, JD

Harold and Jane Hirsh Professor and Chair
Department of Health Policy
School of Public Health and Health Services
The George Washington University

Professor, Health Care Services
School of Medicine
The George Washington University

Moments in Leadership is published by
Pfizer Global Pharmaceuticals, Pfizer Inc, New York, NY.
© 2007 Pfizer Inc. All rights reserved.
The contents do not necessarily reflect the views of Pfizer Inc.
No part of this publication may be reproduced in any form
without prior written permission from the publisher.
Correspondence should be addressed to:
Moments in Leadership,
c/o Executive Director, Public Health and Government, Pfizer Inc
235 East 42nd Street, New York, NY 10017-5755.

ISBN 978-0-9761815-2-1

Printed in Canada.

MOMENTS
IN
LEADERSHIP

CASE STUDIES IN
PUBLIC HEALTH POLICY
AND PRACTICE

Barbara DeBuono, Ana Rita Gonzalez, Sara Rosenbaum Editors

Acknowledgements

$\mathcal{M}$oments in Leadership: Case Studies in Public Health Policy and Practice showcases the extraordinary leadership role of public health professionals and activists in influencing health policy on issues found at the intersection of science, behavior, culture, and society. Through a case study format, the book seeks to do three things. First, it helps readers understand the role of public health professionals and activists in shaping social policy in health and healthcare. Second, the book encourages teachers of public administration, public policy, and public health policy to incorporate strong examples of leadership into their course work. Third, it educates future public health leaders on active engagement in health policy formulation and implementation as a basic tenet of leadership.

Moments in Leadership is the fourth in a series of books published by Pfizer's Public Health and Government group. This series focuses on public health issues and career development. These books are part of our ongoing commitment to building public awareness and understanding of the field of public health. As with our previous publications, Moments in Leadership represents the collective efforts of many individuals who have dedicated countless hours to its development and production. Our sincere thanks go to Dilia Santana of Pfizer Inc, Nadjha Acosta and Sydney Neuhaus of Fleishman-Hillard International Communications, David Farren, and Matt Warhaftig of Warhaftig Associates.

Special thanks must also go to the public health leaders featured in this book. Their work and personal commitment to their causes are truly inspirational. What comes across in each story is the extraordinary humility and generosity of these leaders. Not one of the individuals profiled takes personal credit for his or her achievements; rather, each one always emphasizes the efforts of others. When these individuals are called courageous, they shrug their shoulders and simply state, "I just did what had to be done. Anyone in my position would do the same thing." Of course, history shows this not to be true and makes their examples that much more compelling.

This distinguished group includes:
Abraham Bergman, MD; Carolyn Clancy, MD; Rashi Fein, PhD; Elizabeth Forer, MSW, MPH; Jack Geiger, MD; Lawrence Gostin, JD; Richard N. Gottfried, JD; Edward Hannan, PhD; Ellen Lawton, JD; Lucian Leape, MD; Nicole Lurie, MD, MSPH; J. Michael McGinnis, MD, MPP; Dale Morse, MD, MS; Godfrey Oakley, MD, MSPM; Thomas Perez, JD, MPP; Julius Richmond, MD, MS; Allan Rosenfield, MD; Robert Ross, MD; Joseph Thompson, MD, MPH; Steven Woolf, MD; Patty Young; and Barry Zuckerman, MD. All of these individuals were interviewed for this book and gave generously of their time.

Finally, I am especially grateful to Ana Rita Gonzalez, ScD, and Sara Rosenbaum, JD, the co-editors of *Moments in Leadership*. Their persistence, professionalism, and passion for public health made this book possible.

Barbara DeBuono, MD, MPH
Executive Director
Public Health and Government
Pfizer Inc

Contents

Introduction ————————————————————— I

A Tribute to Allan Rosenfield, MD ————————— 6

Chapter 1.

Forging New Paths: Assuring Access to Healthcare

Introduction ————————————————————— 11
National Case Study: Jack Geiger and the Community
Health Center Movement ————— 14
Local Case Study: Elizabeth Benson Forer and the
Venice Family Clinic ————— 27
Lessons Learned ————————————————— 33

Chapter 2.

Righting Wrongs: Creating Insurance Options for Underserved Populations

Introduction ————————————————————— 37
National Case Study: Rashi Fein and the Creation of
Medicare and Medicaid ————— 40
Local Case Study: Richard Gottfried and SCHIP
in New York ————————— 48
Lessons Learned ————————————————— 53

Chapter 3.

Leveling the Playing Field: Addressing Health Disparities

Introduction ————————————————————— 57
National Case Study: Nicole Lurie, Thomas Perez, and the
Limited English Proficiency Directive —— 62
Local Case Study: Robert Ross and The California
Endowment ————————— 69
Lessons Learned ————————————————— 74

Chapter 4.

Changing the Landscape: Embedding Quality and Patient Safety Into Healthcare Delivery

Introduction _____ 79

National Case Study: Lucian Leape and *To Err Is Human* _____ 84

Local Case Study: Edward Hannan and New York's CABG
Surgery Reporting System _____ 90

Lessons Learned _____ 96

Chapter 5.

No Excuses: Reducing the Risk of Preventable Injury and Disease

Introduction _____ 101

National Case Study: Patty Young and Smoke-Free Airplanes __ 105

Local Case Study: Abraham Bergman and
Bicycle Helmets in Seattle _____ 110

Lessons Learned _____ 113

Chapter 6.

Choosing Health: Improving Individual and Community Health Through Health Promotion Strategies

Introduction _____ 117

National Case Study: Julius Richmond and
the *Healthy People* Report _____ 120

Local Case Study: Joseph Thompson and the Body Mass
Index Assessment Project in Arkansas ___ 127

Lessons Learned _____ 133

Chapter 7.

Walking the Talk: Proving the Case for Prevention

Introduction _____ 137

National Case Study: J. Michael McGinnis, Steven H. Woolf,
and the U.S. Preventive Services
Task Force _____ 141

Local Case Study: Godfrey Oakley and the Fight to
Prevent Spina Bifida With Folic Acid ___ 149

Lessons Learned _____ 155

Chapter 8.

Seeing the Big Picture: Using Epidemiology and Data to Advance Public Health Policy

Introduction ———————————————— 159

National Case Study: Carolyn Clancy and the Agency for
Healthcare Research and Quality ———— 162

Local Case Study: Dale Morse and the New York State
Measles Outbreaks ———————— 167

Lessons Learned ———————————————— 173

Chapter 9.

A Delicate Balance: The Role of Public Health Law in Protecting Individuals' Rights While Safeguarding the Public's Health

Introduction ———————————————— 179

National Case Study: Lawrence Gostin and the Model State
Emergency Health Powers Act ———— 181

Local Case Study: Barry Zuckerman, Ellen Lawton,
and the Medical-Legal Partnership
for Children — Raising the Bar for
Child Health ———————— 192

Lessons Learned ———————————————— 198

Concluding Thoughts ———————————— 203

Introduction

*L*eadership skills are so vital in today's world of public health policy and practice that formal training in this area has become an integral part of public health education. *Moments in Leadership: Case Studies in Public Health Policy and Practice* examines the leadership concept through a human lens. By telling the stories of 21 extraordinary people, while paying tribute to another extraordinary public health professional, *Moments in Leadership* illuminates the ways in which leaders can change the public health landscape.

The individuals and case studies selected for this book are meant to offer readers a rich and multifaceted vision of public health leadership across a wide range of subjects and settings. The people profiled include physicians, epidemiologists, researchers, lawyers, and lawmakers. Their policy landscapes range from local communities to the federal government. Their profiles underscore the interconnectedness between a local intervention affecting a specific time and place, and the broader national climate which can be transformed through policy reform.

Several of the individuals whose work is documented in *Moments in Leadership* had already occupied policy leadership positions when they began the reform efforts; other individuals were completely unknown when they began their work. Some of the stories relate to problems at specific times in the nation's history; others offer examples of innovation that brought new ways of thinking to long-standing problems. All of the stories reveal individuals who focused on a particular issue with clarity of vision and a monumental commitment that helped translate their work into a broader public policy context.

Regardless of time, place, or subject matter, the people in these stories embody the classic characteristics of leadership that have been identified in a considerable body of literature. In their paper, "Public Health Leadership in the 21st Century," Koh and McCormack[1] outline seven elements of public health leadership. These elements, or competencies, promote a model known as the "servant leader" which brings together disparate voices and fosters change through open collaboration while not focusing on who gets the credit. Specifically, these seven competencies are:

1. **The Ability to Acknowledge the Unfamiliar and the Ambiguous**

   Since public health is a field characterized by partial knowledge and uncertain outcomes, the servant leader most often faces an ambiguous environment that requires adaptive work. Learning is required to both define the problem and to implement a solution. Leading people through the unfamiliar allows the leader to act as an instrument of change.

2. **The Ability to Cultivate the Higher Value of Interdependence**

   Servant leaders must create a space where others can be invited in while recognizing that actions may trigger repercussions and changes to the existing policy landscape.

3. **The Ability to Recognize Crisis Leadership as an Evolving Part of Public Health**

   Planning for the unthinkable means promoting systematic preparedness that cuts across all dimensions of society.

4. **An Understanding of the "Public" Part of Public Health Leadership**

   Public health leaders are always on stage and, consequently, must be prepared for comment, criticism, and interpretation (or misinterpretation), which at times can be hurtful and threatening.

5. **Sensitivity to and Respect for the Community**

   Scenario planning is a way to engage multiple stakeholders, with a leader bringing together a diverse group of people to envision the future.

6. **The Capacity to Nurture the Spirit**

   Public health leaders often use their own pain as motivation to help prevent suffering for others. At the same time, these leaders focus on expressing themselves rather than proving themselves.

7. **The Ability to Hone Succinct and Concrete Communication**

   To be heard through the cacophony of the mass media, public health leaders need to address themes in simple, yet powerful, ways that will appeal to the average person and that will help sway his or her behavior.

Not every public health leader can be expected to have all seven competencies in equal measure. *Moments in Leadership* demonstrates how leaders exhibiting different competencies can achieve their policy goals.

Moments in Leadership is a kaleidoscope. This book presents public health policymaking in contexts that differ in color and texture yet are sustained by common elements. The profiles underscore the fact that traits essential to leadership in public health policy are those that are associated with leadership in general; that is, technical knowledge, imaginative and innovative thinking, a willingness to take responsibility, social skills and emotional balance, the ability to rapidly adapt to changing circumstances, creativity and independence, great courage, a willingness to fail and to be wrong, vision and commitment that support forward motion even in the face of stacked odds, and a commitment to social justice and the common good.[2] With this kind of leadership, enormous gains in public health policy have been realized. Without it, advancing the field would be difficult, if not impossible.[3]

Advancing policy to address the social, economic, or healthcare needs of a population requires careful analysis, planning, and evaluation. The policymaking process is fairly constant, regardless of the situation or setting. And it can take various routes because of constraints of time, training, complexity of the problem, resource availability, and organizational affiliation.[4] At the same time, it is possible to identify four basic stages that are common to all policy reform endeavors and that together form a policy cycle.

1. **The first stage** involves gaining an understanding of the problem to be addressed by defining the problem, learning the policy context for the problem, and identifying stakeholders (individuals or parties who have a direct interest in an issue), along with their key roles.

2. **The second stage** entails developing solutions by collecting information and evidence; identifying, weighing, and analyzing options for their cost and impact; consulting widely with stakeholders and knowledgeable people; and forming and motivating coalitions of individuals and interests that have a shared stake in the outcome.

3. **The third stage** is implementing solutions by communicating about policy reform, supporting implementation efforts through training and advisement, and testing different options.

4. **The fourth and final stage** is testing success by evaluating implementation, making adjustments, and seeking additional reforms, thus completing the cycle.

Readers will see all four stages in the following profiles.

Moments in Leadership is intended for a wide range of readers who are eager to learn the skills and techniques of leadership and who are willing to effect change by influencing public health policy. The book follows an organizational approach that is grounded in the core functions and essential services of public health. In its landmark study, *The Future of Public Health* (1988), the Institute of Medicine (IOM) developed a simple and elegant framework for thinking about the essential nature of public health. The IOM identified the functions of assessment, assurance, and policy development as its core functional activities. These core functions were later amplified by the United States Department of Health and Human Services into a series of "essential services"[5] that carry out public health's basic role in ensuring "the conditions necessary for people to live healthy lives through communitywide prevention and protection programs."[6] These essential services are:

- ► Monitoring health status

- ► Diagnosing health problems

- ► Informing and empowering people

- ► Developing policies

- ► Linking people to health services

- ► Evaluating quality, mobilizing community partnerships, and enforcing laws and regulations

- ► Ensuring a competent work force

- ► Conducting research for new insights

The stories in *Moments in Leadership* reflect these core functions and essential services. Such issues as access to healthcare, health promotion, disease prevention, and the use of law to protect the public health are covered in case studies throughout the book. *Moments in Leadership* concludes with a synthesizing chapter that weaves together leadership and policymaking theories with the leadership stories in order to identify major lessons for future policy-influencing efforts.

Moments in Leadership reveals how the passion of one individual who is willing to stand up and use his or her extraordinary skills and vision can achieve a public health goal. Of course, each of these important contributions would not have been achieved without a larger group of committed colleagues and supporters. However, by serving as a catalyst to spark awareness of and action on a public health issue, each individual undergoes a transformation from an interested observer into an active leader. It is these moments of transformation and action on which *Moments in Leadership* focuses. ❋

References

1. Koh HK, McCormack M; Center for Public Leadership at Harvard University. Public health leadership in the 21st century. 2006 [cited 2006 Dec 1]. Available from: http://www.ksg.harvard.edu/leadership/research/publications/papers/2006/7_publichealth.pdf.

2. Koh HK, McCormack M; Center for Public Leadership at Harvard University. Public health leadership in the 21st century. 2006 [cited 2006 Dec 1]. Available from: http://www.ksg.harvard.edu/leadership/research/publications/papers/2006/7_publichealth.pdf.

3. Beecher EC, Chassin MR Taking health care back: a physician's role in quality improvement. *Academic Medicine.* 2002; 77: 953-62.

4. Koh HK, McCormack M; Center for Public Leadership at Harvard University. Public health leadership in the 21st century. 2006 [cited 2006 Dec 1]. Available from: http://www.ksg.harvard.edu/leadership/research/publications/papers/2006/7_publichealth.pdf.

5. Centers for Disease Control and Prevention. Atlanta: The essential public health services. [cited 2006 Oct 1]. Available from: http://www.cdc.gov/od/ocphp/nphpsp/EssentialPHServices.htm.

6. Harrell J, Baker E. The essential services of public health. [cited 2006 Oct 1]. Available from: http://www.apha.org/ppp/science/10ES.html.

A Tribute to Allan Rosenfield, MD

Allan Rosenfield, MD

This book is dedicated to Allan Rosenfield, MD, a public health pioneer in the field of reproductive, maternal, and child health. His writings on maternal mortality have had an important impact on public health policy. When Rosenfield first learned that more than 500,000 women die each year of complications caused by pregnancy and childbirth, he set about to change this stark reality. Throughout his distinguished 40-year career, he has never lost sight of the "maternal" in maternal and child health (MCH). Thanks to his pioneering efforts, public health policies are now much more responsive to maternal health, fostering remarkable progress in women's health throughout the world.

As the dean of the Mailman School of Public Health at Columbia University in New York City since 1986, Rosenfield has been guiding the school to pre-eminence among schools of public health in the United States. His career in the field happened by accident — not unlike many other public health professionals. After graduating from Columbia's College of Physicians and Surgeons, he followed his father's lead and trained in obstetrics and planned a career delivering babies in Boston, his hometown. Before completing his residency, he was drafted into the Air Force, where he served at the Osan Air Force Base in South Korea. He frequently traveled beyond the base into the countryside and witnessed the public health conditions in the poor, rural areas. Following his Air Force service and the completion of his residency in 1966, he accepted a one-year position to teach obstetrics and gynecology in Nigeria at the new University of Lagos Teaching Hospital. While there, Rosenfield saw firsthand the need to increase emergency obstetrical care for poor expectant mothers who were dying at alarming rates from complications of pregnancy, as well as the need to make voluntary family planning services more widely available. There, his lifelong passion first caught fire — emphasizing maternal health as central to family health.

Before leaving Nigeria in mid-1967, Rosenfield was offered a job by The Population Council to work in Thailand in the area of family planning and reproductive health. Thinking he would stay for no more than one year, he once again postponed his plan to begin a practice in obstetrics. He worked at the Ministry of Public Health and ended up living in Thailand for six years. Interestingly, his last delivery was his daughter, who was born in Thailand.

Rosenfield worked very closely with the Family Health Division of Thailand's Ministry of Public Health and helped launch the first national family planning program. The ruling government was not ready to establish a national family planning policy, but the under-secretary of the Ministry of Public Health began preparations, nonetheless, for such a program. Thailand was a country in its first years of a rapid move toward modernity, and Thai women were independent by nature. An important study in the early 1960s demonstrated that Thai women were interested in family planning services.

At that time, prescriptions for birth control pills could be written only by physicians, who were too few, especially, in rural areas. There, the population pressure was the greatest. Rosenfield developed a study to test the safety of auxiliary midwives in providing oral contraceptives by using a simple checklist. At the same time, these auxiliary midwives would educate rural people about family planning. The study was so successful that the number of sites dispensing birth control pills soon grew from 100 to more than 3,000. Thanks to this successful study and the commitment of key ministry personnel, the National Family Planning Program soon became one of Asia's most successful family planning programs. A number of ministry officials, particularly Dr. Winich Asavena and Sonsak Varakamin, were critical to the program's success. Avasena and Varakamin were joined by Mechai Viravaidya, a leading charismatic figure in the private sector. Viravaidya, a Thai educated in Australia, created a private family planning organization that worked in collaboration with the Ministry of Public Health.

Rosenfield's passion for improving the health of women transformed him from an obstetrician into an acknowledged expert in population-based health. Upon his return from Thailand, he joined the Columbia faculty at both the School of Public Health and the College of Physicians and Surgeons and has been a full-fledged academic ever since.

Rosenfield's approach to maternal health incorporates a belief that high quality healthcare for pregnant women must be widely available. While acknowledging the strong feelings that abortion can stir, he states that teenage girls and women who do not wish to be pregnant will find any means that are available to them to terminate their pregnancies. He believes that interventions for complications of pregnancy must be accessible and delivered by trained healthcare professionals. This, too, has been a guiding principle of Rosenfield's work.

When the worldwide AIDS epidemic unfolded in the 1980s and 1990s, Rosenfield became more involved in the global issues of HIV/AIDS. As programs were being developed to prevent maternal-to-child transmission (PMTCT) of HIV, he became a champion for mothers who must also have access to HIV/AIDS care and treatment. In 2002, Rosenfield and the Mailman School of Public Health started a new program, MTCT-Plus, to focus on care and treatment for women and their children. Selecting specific areas in seven countries in sub-Saharan Africa and in Thailand, the Mailman School secured grants from eight private foundations and the United States Agency for International Development to support interventions.

In 2004, the national Centers for Disease Control and Prevention awarded the Mailman School a $125 million five-year grant through President Bush's Emergency Plan for AIDS Relief, the largest in Columbia University's history. The grant made possible a new program, the Multicountry Columbia Antiretroviral Program (MCAP), expanding MTCT-Plus approaches to families and communities in larger geographic areas. Reflecting Rosenfield's leadership, Columbia

University uses existing infrastructure and fully integrates its work into local healthcare systems, consistent with national plans in each country. The university also created the International Center for AIDS Care and Treatment Programs as the organizational umbrella for the university's MTCT-Plus, MCAP, and other AIDS care and treatment efforts, which are directed by infectious disease specialist Dr. Wafaa El-Sadr.

Rosenfield also applies his vision and leadership to the unique health needs of adolescents and addresses issues such as sex education, birth control, and maternal healthcare. Taking a keen interest in the low-income neighborhoods surrounding the Mailman School of Public Health, he strengthened Columbia's ties to the community by founding a family planning and reproductive health program that is focused on adolescent women. In addition, Columbia founded the Young Men's Clinic, where teenage boys can receive exams by physicians and learn about various health matters, including sexually transmitted diseases and birth control.

One of Rosenfield's enduring legacies is the addition of the name "Mailman" to Columbia's School of Public Health in 1997. Thanks to his work with the Mailman Foundation, a family-run foundation that supports institutions concerned with child welfare, education, and the environment, he secured a $33 million naming gift for the school. This gift has helped the school to attract other gifts and substantial grants, elevating it to one of the country's leading schools of public health.

Rosenfield was diagnosed with amyotrophic lateral sclerosis, or Lou Gehrig's disease, in December 2005. It is an irreversible disease of the neuromuscular system and follows different courses in different people. Although he can no longer ski or play tennis, nor board a flight to Dhaka, Bangladesh, which he once would do for one-day conferences, he continues to work every day. He considers himself fortunate because his health remained good into his 70s and because he has the support of a wonderful family. His colleagues around the world recognize his contributions to public health, particularly women's health. For his work, he has received numerous awards and honors.

Rosenfield perceives that there is a growing appreciation for public health, particularly among college students and graduate students in schools of medicine, nursing, and other areas of the health sciences. He has helped students focus on the status of women's health and, specifically, reproductive and maternal health. Thanks to many advocates, researchers, practitioners, and policymakers who followed him, the *M* in MCH has won its deserved place in public health.

According to Rosenfield, a leader should listen and then work toward consensus. Leadership should neither be a top-down process nor imperious. As he says, "You lead when you get people to come along with you." By every measure, he is a leader. As a positive result of his career that began by accident, public health policy involving maternal and child health will never be the same. ❁

Chapter I. **Forging New Paths:**
            Assuring Access to Healthcare

Introduction

$\mathcal{T}$he years of the Lyndon B. Johnson administration were a watershed in the political, economic, social, and intellectual life of the nation. They stretched from the assassination of John F. Kennedy in November 1963 through Johnson's landslide election in November 1964 to his decision in March 1968 not to seek re-election in the contentious Vietnam War era. It was during the Johnson years when the parameters of the modern social contract came into view and when society began to establish certain basic principles regarding how the healthcare system should function for all people. Although access to affordable healthcare remains an elusive challenge today, the strides that have been made over the past four decades can still be seen as monumental.

●

The 1960s were an era in which civil rights, social justice, economic advancement, and educational and intellectual achievement came together to form a societal "big bang."

● The 1960s were an era in which civil rights, social justice, economic advancement, and educational and intellectual achievement came together to form a societal "big bang." The decade witnessed the culmination of the civil rights movement in a series of groundbreaking laws aimed at ending racial segregation and ensuring the right of all people to fully participate in the political, economic, and social life of the nation. The decade also produced the major laws that help define modern American society in such areas as health insurance for the elderly and the poor, education, housing, nutrition, and social welfare. The list of legislative achievements during that time is extraordinary: the creation of Medicare and Medicaid, the Elementary and Secondary Education and Higher Education Acts of 1965, the Fair Housing Act, the Civil Rights Act of 1964, and the Voting Rights Act of 1965. The 1960s were also a decade of great experimentation in assisting poor communities, with an unfolding (and controversial) public policy effort to find the right combination of investments, incentives, and supports that would enable low-income urban and rural communities to open the door to the American dream for their residents.

In 1965, healthcare in many poor communities was, for all practical purposes, nonexistent. When the first experimental health centers opened that year in Mound Bayou, Miss., and Boston, Mass., the nation's African-American poverty rate stood at 42 percent.[1]   ●   Health insurance statistics from the era suggest that health benefits were basically unknown. Entire communities lacked drinkable water and indoor plumbing and had poorly equipped hospitals. Voting rights for African-American adults in the South were still a dream deferred, and the battle following Brown v. Board of Education was raging at its worst in many places. Indeed, only two years had passed since Congress repealed express legislative authority to build segregated facilities as part of the Hospital Survey and Construction Act. This act, known as Hill Burton, authorized the expenditure of billions of dollars in federal hospital construction loans and grants.

> ●
>
> Health insurance statistics from the era suggest that health benefits were basically unknown.

The transformation that would be brought about by social investments, such as Medicaid and the health centers program, could hardly be imagined. In the mid-1960s, the notion of affordable public health insurance for poor people was unknown; indeed, in thousands of rural communities, the basic concept of hospital births for poor infants was foreign. In 1965, one in every 23 black infants died before his or her first birthday;[2] in the Mississippi Delta, the figures were as high as 60 per 1,000 live births,[3] and half of these births were outside a hospital.[4] Furthermore, the post-neonatal death rate among the black population in Mississippi in 1965 was 26 per 1,000 live births. This is 30 percent greater than the rate in Alabama, more than two times greater than the rates among blacks in Illinois and New York, and five times the rates for white infants in these four states.[5]

It was at this turning point in American history — at the juncture of politics and policy and social, economic, and healthcare justice — that the health centers movement was born. The early health centers, a modest demonstration program, were the brainchild of a small group of healthcare visionaries and social activists. Fresh from Mississippi's seminal 1964 Freedom Summer, they convinced an equally visionary group of federal officials to launch an experiment not only to get basic healthcare to impoverished urban and rural communities but also to fundamentally redefine the concepts of healthcare and community governance.

● The pioneering effort to develop the modern health center as both a practical and public policy concept centers on Jack Geiger, MD. The spirit of the original health centers movement lives on today, not only in a mature network of federally supported centers throughout the United States, but also in the continuing reliance on healthcare as a means of bringing social investment into poor communities. Without Dr. Geiger and the enduring importance of primary care clinical leadership, the free clinic movement might never have happened. Perhaps the best example of this is the Venice Family Clinic in Los Angeles. This clinic has evolved since its founding in 1970 into the largest free clinic in the country. Unlike community health centers, which rely primarily on Medicaid and Medicare for their funding, free clinics rely less on government and more on community partnerships and private and foundation fundraising in order to serve the medically indigent. As the following two case studies illustrate, both community health centers and free clinics have proved to be successful in helping solve the problem of access to care for the most underserved populations. ✿

●
The pioneering effort to develop the modern health center as both a practical and public policy concept centers on Jack Geiger, MD.

National Case Study

Jack Geiger and the Community Health Center Movement

Jack Geiger, MD

$\mathcal{N}$o individual exercised more leadership than Jack Geiger in advancing access to care through primary prevention, nor can anyone tell the story of community health centers better than the champion of the movement himself. In 1965, from his base at Tufts University School of Medicine in Boston, Geiger founded and managed the first two centers in the United States, one at Columbia Point in Boston; the other, in rural Mississippi at Mound Bayou in Bolivar County. Since 1965, in a signal achievement for public health policy, the network of community health centers throughout the nation has expanded to nearly 1,000. Community health centers have changed thousands of communities over the last 40 years — an achievement very few model programs ever attain.

Geiger likes to say that there is a difference between an institution in a community, such as a subway stop, and a true community institution. By definition, a health center is a community institution. First, in its own staffing, a center generally reflects the diversity of the population for which it works. Second, while a center is not the only institution in a community providing access to care, its ongoing care makes it a much more integral part of the community. The center impacts the health of the whole community, not just an individual patient.

The idea of community health centers appeared to Geiger in 1957 while he was working side by side with Sidney and Emily Kark in South Africa, thanks to a Rockefeller Foundation fellowship during his senior year at Western Reserve Medical School. By the mid-1950s, the Karks had established 40 community health centers throughout South Africa, starting with the great rural model in Pholela in the early 1940s. Pholela was a 500-square-mile Zulu tribal reserve 100 miles north of Durban in Natal Province. Geiger worked there and also at the Lamontville Health Center in a Zulu housing project on the edge of Durban. In the early 1950s, the Karks had successfully persuaded the apartheid advocates who governed South Africa that the health of African workers, the bulk of the South African work force, was important. The apartheid government approved their notion that community health centers should reach African workers, combining public health and clinical medicine under one roof in both rural and urban settings. In 1959, as apartheid grew increasingly repressive, the Verwoerd government shut the centers down, thwarting the Karks' plans to expand their number to 400.

Like many other young white people in the mid-1960s, Geiger became deeply involved in the civil rights movement. In 1964 and in response to President Lyndon Johnson's War on Poverty and the recent Civil Rights Act, he participated in the voter registration drive in Mississippi, known as the Freedom Summer.

●

[Geiger] realized, as he looked around, that his dreams of a career in international health could better be addressed in the U.S.

●   He realized, as he looked around, that his dreams of a career in international health could better be addressed in the U.S. He also recalled the moment at Western Reserve, as he struggled to secure the Rockefeller Foundation grant, when he looked out a hospital window and "It occurred to me that out there in Cleveland, who got sick and who didn't, and what they got sick with, and what happened to them made healthcare as much a social phenomenon as a biological one. I got very excited, believing I had just invented social medicine." A quick check through the library stacks, however, revealed that the Germans and British had already been doing it for a hundred years.

In December 1964 at a meeting of Freedom Summer veterans in Greenville, Miss., Geiger suggested to a receptive audience that his experience at Pholela could be replicated if a medical school from the North came to Mississippi and established a full-scale comprehensive community health center. Enthusiastic approval and further programmatic suggestions came from Dr. Robert Smith (the black physician from Jackson, Miss., who headed the effort to provide medical care to civil rights workers), Dr. Desmond Callan (who later initiated one of the earliest community health centers in New York City), and others. The chairman of preventive medicine at Tufts, Dr. Count Gibson, also a Freedom Summer veteran, was at that meeting and assured Geiger that Tufts would sponsor the center if funding could be found. Gibson recognized that Geiger's vision, which was influenced by the civil rights movement, addressed such abstract issues as race, poverty, and social justice in remarkably concrete ways.

In January 1965, Geiger visited Washington, D.C., and met with Sanford Kravitz, the director of Research and Demonstrations at the newly created Office of Economic Opportunity (OEO). Until his visit, the OEO deferred to the Department of Health, Education and Welfare (HEW) on all issues involving healthcare. Kravitz had just become aware, however, that data from Head Start and the Job Corps demonstrated huge unmet health needs. After three hours of conversation, ● Geiger requested $30,000 for a feasibility study of a community health center — the classic academic shuffle, as he calls it. Kravitz said that wouldn't do and countered that he would fund Geiger with $300,000 if he got right to work. Excited, Geiger returned to Tufts and began constructing a budget. He realized three things right away: that $300,000 was far below the funding necessary, that involvement by Tufts in Mississippi would sorely aggravate Boston neighbors who had their own unmet needs, and that the Mississippi white power structure would resist. In view of the OEO's promise of support and Kravitz's impatience, the obstacles were quickly overcome. Tufts proposed two community health centers, one nearby at the Columbia Point Housing Project on Dorchester Bay in Boston (in the district of Speaker of the House John McCormick) and the other in a deliberately unspecified rural area in the South (to keep potentially hostile Southern congressional delegations at bay). The total budget was now $1.2 million, a far cry from Geiger's original $30,000 request. Although

●

Geiger requested $30,000 for a feasibility study of a community health center. Kravitz said that wouldn't do and countered that he would fund Geiger with $300,000 if he got right to work.

politicians tangled over specifics and the OEO swallowed hard, the grant won approval in June 1965.

On Dec. 11, 1965, the Columbia Point Health Center opened — a remarkable one-year turnaround from the meeting in Greenville. The Columbia Point facility occupied several renovated apartments in a housing project on Dorchester Bay. Columbia Point had a colorful history, first as a prisoner-of-war camp, then as a garbage dump, and then as the site of the public housing project for 8,000 low-income residents. The health center, located on a peninsula, was cut off by two expressways and a rail line and had no ready access to public transportation. Later, the Kennedy Presidential Library would be built on a nearby point of land, along with the Boston campus of the University of Massachusetts. Over time, the housing project evolved into a mixed-use apartment complex featuring luxury and middle-income units, leaving less than 400 units set aside for low-income people. When the health center opened in 1965, however, the housing project residents were relieved to not have to spend three hours each way traveling to and from Boston hospitals and outpatient departments for care.

As President Johnson shaped the War on Poverty, governors from the South won a concession that they could veto any OEO project in their own states. There were exceptions, however. OEO Director Sargent Shriver could override a veto, although that would likely cost too much political capital in a sharply divided Congress. The OEO depended on Congress to refund it each year, and Congress — like the nation — was embroiled in the ongoing civil rights struggle. More relevant to Geiger's plans, however, was that the governors could not veto a grant offered through an institution of higher education. Believing that they could control their own state universities and even win funding through them, these governors did not foresee that a Northern university could be equally exempt from their veto. This exception allowed Geiger to carefully evaluate the best possible site for the rural community health center, which would be sponsored by Tufts. Geiger chose northern Bolivar County in Mississippi, about 100 miles south of Memphis along the Mississippi River. His choice stemmed from the fact that in Bolivar County, with one of the poorest black populations in the country, a health center would document the enormous burdens of sickness, malnutrition, and premature death and show that they could be overcome. He also welcomed a return to Mississippi, where he had spent the memorable Freedom Summer of 1964.

Bolivar County has two county seats, one on the river (Rosedale) and one inland (Cleveland). Since the river is prone to flooding, inland Cleveland, amid the cotton and soybean fields of the largely agricultural county, became the important center. The specific site, to serve an area of 500 square miles, became Mound Bayou, the oldest all-black town in the country, located 10 miles north of Cleveland. The median black family income in Bolivar County was $600 a year, and black infant mortality, although underreported because of the large proportion of home births without physicians, was thought to be at least 90 per 1,000 births. Maternal mortality was equally horrifying.

● The first community health centers had two policy goals: to remove barriers to access by eliminating ability to pay as a factor and to unite public health and clinical medicine under one roof. In addition, a third policy goal became quickly apparent. The community must be involved in the decision-making for the centers.

After much planning and recruiting of key support personnel, Geiger and his colleagues arrived in Mound Bayou to begin their work. Pressing needs confronted them immediately. First, they had to hire and train a staff that would address the health needs of a population that had been poorly served, if at all. The area had two small hospitals, one with 20 beds and another with 40 beds, and both run by black fraternal orders. During the first year and while the health center was still under construction, the work involved health education, community organizing, public health

●

The first community health centers had two policy goals: to remove barriers to access by eliminating ability to pay as a factor and to unite public health and clinical medicine under one roof.

nursing, and midwifery. Geiger and his staff converted an old parsonage into the first clinical center, with the living room as the waiting room, two bedrooms as examining rooms, and the kitchen as the lab. ● On the first day, 10 people showed up. On the second day, 20. On the third, 85.

●

On the first day, 10 people showed up. On the second day, 20. On the third, 85.

The initial OEO grant omitted dentists. But in the end, they too joined physicians, nurses, nurse midwives, public health nurses, sanitarians, environmental engineers, social workers, health educators, and community organizers to form the center's staff. The health center gave priority to hiring local people but also persuaded black professionals now living in the North, but originally from the South, to return and assist in the venture.

In northern Bolivar County, the incidence of infant diarrheal disease was frightening. Treating this illness in the hospital cost an average of $500 per infant, with little hope that the infant would be immune to recurring illness once out of the hospital. Digging a well with clean water, on the other hand, cost about $65, and building a sanitary privy cost about $100. One of the largest operations of the center turned out to be the building of hundreds of sanitary privies and the digging of hundreds of protected wells. Other vital operations included repairs to housing and eliminating disease vectors, such as rats, mosquitoes, flies, and snakes. Removing pesticides from the environment also turned out to be one of the most effective health measures. Another was to equip a traveling van with a portable generator, clean water and food, medicine, and a hospital bed with IV poles, and to staff it with a public health nurse. Now a child with viral encephalitis could be treated at home — perhaps a plantation shack — while the mother was educated to continue proper treatment. People who were exposed to good healthcare became much more responsive to health education and much more willing to change their behaviors.

One of the most urgent problems confronting the health center staff was severe malnutrition, particularly in infants, which often appeared along with other infections. The outcomes could be devastating. There was neither a food stamp program then nor effective commodity surplus distributions. State welfare payments reached less than a third of those eligible and, by Mississippi's own standards, provided less than a third of the amount necessary for healthy survival. Many children ate only one inadequate meal a day, and some families desperately tried to gather pecans or shoot squirrels for food. The health center determined to save these sick infants and began by stocking food — powdered milk, eggs, and the like — in the parsonage. Then community organizer John Hatch devised a better plan.

There were 10 towns in the northern Bolivar County target area, each serving a rural hinterland and each with a black grocery store. ● Whenever center physicians saw a sick, malnourished infant without adequate support, they wrote prescriptions for food — a certain amount of milk, meat, fruits, and vegetables — for that infant and its siblings for two weeks or more until the illness was under control. These prescriptions were processed through the center's social service department and called a "loan" in order to avoid the stigma of charity. Mothers then took these prescriptions to be filled at the black grocery stores, which in turn sent the bills to the health center's pharmacy department for reimbursement.

> ●
> Whenever center physicians saw a sick, malnourished infant without adequate support, they wrote prescriptions for food.

This emergency system worked well and without abuse until the hostile state government, deciding that Soviet-style communism had somehow arrived in the Delta, complained to the OEO. That agency sent an emissary to Mound Bayou shouting that the program was illegal because, clearly, a health center pharmacy was intended only to disperse drugs for the treatment of disease. Geiger's response was equally clear. Every medical textbook, he said, agreed that the best treatment of malnutrition was food. The program survived.

But Hatch had an even better idea. He knew that the mechanization of cotton agriculture and the government's policy of paying farmers to restrict cotton acreage had left thousands of sharecroppers unemployed, making malnutrition inevitable. But they still had superb agricultural skills, and vacant land was available. So Hatch organized the Northern Bolivar Farm Cooperative using private foundation grants to rent and buy rich farmland. A thousand northern Bolivar County black families pooled their labor to grow vegetables, not cotton, and to share in the crop according to the days of labor they had put in. The farm coop grew hundreds of tons of vegetables each year. Hatch and the local population had invented a new occupation — nutritional sharecropping — and solved a major threat to health. The health center's leadership, in other words, had created not just clinical success but environmental improvement, nutritional stability, and new opportunities for employment and local leadership.

●

An aspect of community health centers not fully appreciated is how they impact, in a multi-generational way, the educational aspirations of the local population.

● An aspect of community health centers not fully appreciated is how they impact, in a multigenerational way, the educational aspirations of the local population. A wonderful example during Geiger's time in northern Bolivar County was L.C. Dorsey. She became a health educator after having worked beside Fannie Lou Hamer, the political leader who succeeded in seating her alternate integrated delegation at the 1964 Democratic National Convention. With only a ninth-grade education, Dorsey earned her high school equivalency in a program run by the center's Office of Education that Geiger and Hatch had the foresight to establish as a pathway to health careers for local residents. She became a deputy director and then director of the Northern Bolivar Farm Cooperative for several years.

She enrolled at the State University of New York at Stony Brook Graduate School of Social Work and earned her Master of Social Work degree with honors. She returned to Mississippi, worked as a social worker for the Delta Ministry in a prison project, and put all six of her children through college. Not content to stop learning, she enrolled at Howard University and earned her Doctor in Social Work degree and a certificate in health management from Johns Hopkins University. Dorsey returned to Mound Bayou and took Geiger's old job as executive director of the Delta Health Center, where she had begun work decades earlier.

The health center's Office of Education, headed first by Clay Simpson, taught the high school equivalency program, a college preparatory course, and extensive in-service training programs for local staff. The median educational level of black people in northern Bolivar County was fifth grade and from inferior segregated schools. Owing much to the interventions of the Office of Education, Geiger believes that more than 100 people from black families in northern Bolivar County are now in the health profession at some level, from technicians to physicians.

In the first decade alone, these included seven MDs and five PhDs in the clinical sciences — including two sisters from Alligator, Miss., population 900 — and the first 10 registered black sanitarians in Mississippi history. The center's influence in that first decade also produced approximately 20 registered nurses and an equal number of licensed practical nurses, two environmental engineers, and six social workers. Two of the original students who had entered a special program at Tufts Medical School returned to the Delta Health Center after their residency training, one as a pediatrician and the other as a clinical director.

● The center has learned of the first grandchild to earn a doctorate — the newest generation to feel the center's positive effect. When Geiger asks health center directors around the country about the staff they hire from the local community, the directors concur with his own observation that the first thing staff members do with their salaries is to buy a house. This is almost always followed by the second thing, which is to send their children to college. Although these findings have yet to be quantified in a systematic way, Geiger is certain that they are true and part of the untold story of the positive impact of community health centers.

● The center has learned of the first grandchild to earn a doctorate — the newest generation to feel the center's positive effect.

In 1975, when the centers moved from OEO to HEW (now the Department of Health and Human Services, or HHS), legislation required that they be constituted as not-for-profit corporations with elected boards of governors, and that at least half of the seated board members use the centers for their own healthcare.

Known as the 51 Percent Rule, the centers consequently became the only part of the American healthcare system in which patients and the community help govern the health policies and health programs of their own primary care providers. Initially, the centers relied on federal grants for funding but once Congress enacted Medicaid later in 1965, it quickly became and continues to be a major source of health center revenue.

As community health centers evolved nationwide, laws were enacted that required the centers to conduct an assessment of the health status of their target population every two years. Over the years, at least 60 independent studies have documented that community health centers offer superior quality in primary care. Unfortunately, as the cost of medical care has escalated, funding is sometimes separated from what works best: public health interventions, health education, and environmental controls. Instead, funding is often restricted to the delivery of personal medical services.

For many centers, Section 330 grants from HHS account for as little as 15 percent of annual revenue, while Medicaid accounts for a third to more than half. Sliding self-payment scales have grown increasingly important as a source of revenue. The most successful centers have been agile in securing local and state grants as well as support from private foundations in order to expand their programs, particularly in environmental controls. In the future, universal use of electronic medical records promises to make community health centers even more effective in the way they respond to their populations. With a mission to serve a defined area and a defined population, community health centers should be able to continually improve the way they bring medical care to that population.

In the competitive marketplace of medical care, community health centers have the advantage of knowing their populations. One size does not fit all, however, even with community health centers. For example, migrant-worker programs and school-based programs may differ considerably in size from those in large urban centers. The 51 Percent Rule for the governing board means that community health centers will continue to be responsive to their populations in the way they allocate resources, leading to the possibility of very different approaches by urban and rural centers. Geiger gives an example from the Columbia Point Health Center, where garbage trucks entered a garbage dump nearby at all hours of the day. This created a health hazard for small children who were being hit by trucks on the average of once a week. Closing the garbage dump became the public health solution, one that the community could support because it brought immediate public health benefits to its own backyard.

Geiger believes that, as a general rule, urban centers confront more complex problems than rural centers because of the breakdown of family structures and the problems of intense racial residential segregation. These complex problems mean that urban community health centers, no matter how effective they have been, cannot stand as islands but must seek interagency collaboration to ensure a healthy future.

A looming concern for the continued success of community health centers is the low number of medical students choosing primary care careers. Would-be dermatologists, anesthesiologists, and radiologists fill residency programs, while internal medicine and family medicine residencies have vacancies. Whether these choices are dictated by lifestyle or remuneration, something must be done about the lack of trained primary care physicians.

●   Another vital skill that Geiger came to appreciate is the role that social workers and community organizers play in the success of community health centers. Physicians, by training, thrive in hierarchical systems, and many do not acquire the skills necessary for building consensus within communities. Another key player who Geiger wishes he had been able to recruit early on was a skilled epidemiologist. With accurate assessments of the impact of the center's work, processes could have been fine-tuned earlier rather than later.

Another vital skill that Geiger came to appreciate is the role that social workers and community organizers play in the success of community health centers.

●

Geiger's vision and hard work helped establish a national movement for federally funded community health centers. The sequence leading to this national movement began in 1966 with a visit by Sen. Edward M. Kennedy to the Columbia Point Health Center. He was so impressed that when he returned to Washington, he became a major force in promoting the idea to Congress. Ever since that visit, healthcare has been Kennedy's legislative passion. Geiger and others helped Kennedy draft legislation that created an Office of Health Affairs within the OEO and that appropriated $100 million, initially, to fund community health centers. Nearly all of the initial proposals were aligned with schools of medicine. ● Ultimately, members of Congress competed with each other to win federal funding for centers in their own districts. Opposition from the American Medical Association (AMA), community hospitals, and even some black physicians, who initially viewed community health centers as competitors, soon faded as the benefits for underserved populations became apparent. Most of the centers, even those in urban areas, serve populations that were so limited in their access to healthcare, and whose facilities were so poor, that no one could argue with the need.

●

Ultimately, members of Congress competed with each other to win federal funding for centers in their own districts.

With community involvement being key to governing the centers, political backers quickly lined up. In 1975 when there were 150 centers, Dr. George A. Silver, HEW deputy assistant secretary, called for 800 centers. These centers were to serve not only rural and urban areas but also migrant workers, the homeless, public housing projects, and schools. Some were quite small; others, very big. In 2006, nearly 1,000 centers were serving 15 million people, numbers that Geiger and his colleagues could hardly have imagined as they began their work at Columbia Point and Mound Bayou.

Of the many distinguished people who Geiger has met in his career, perhaps the most inspirational was the great anthropologist Margaret Mead. She had a way of cutting through barriers, and her quote "Never underestimate the ability of a small group of determined people to change the world" resonates with him. He recounts with delight the time he and Mead arrived together at the Harvard Club in New York City for a speaking engagement. Rather than using the entrance reserved for women, she, with cape and walking stick in hand, marched directly through the main entrance into the club's reception room, defying anyone to say a word. No one did. At an American Association for the Advancement of Science meeting in Boston in 1969 where she was the named lecturer, she asked for Geiger's advice on who might be a worthy recipient of her $1,000 honorarium. Not only did she accept his advice, she arranged for L.C. Dorsey to accept the check in person on behalf of the Northern Bolivar Farm Cooperative. ✸

Local Case Study

Elizabeth Benson Forer
and the Venice Family Clinic

*Elizabeth Forer,
MSW, MPH*

$\mathcal{T}$hanks to the successful models established by Jack Geiger at Columbia Point and Mound Bayou, the community health center movement has flourished throughout the United States. Community health centers have become numerous. They have transformed communities both large and small, in urban and rural areas, and with specific populations, such as migrant workers. The movement has also fostered alternative approaches to gaining access to care for low-income populations. One such approach, the free clinic, represents a new aspect of public health policy and owes much to the community health center movement.

The Venice Family Clinic in Venice, Calif., offers access to healthcare in poorer neighborhoods of western Los Angeles. The uninsured population in Los Angeles is thought to number at least two million. To those who are able to reach the clinic, healthcare is free. Thanks to more than 2,400 individuals, including 519 physicians who volunteer their time, the free healthcare provided by the clinic is high quality.

Founded in 1970 in a borrowed storefront dental clinic by Dr. Philip Rossman and Dr. Mayer Davidson, the Venice Family Clinic today operates seven locations in Venice and neighboring Culver City, Mar Vista, and Santa Monica. Today, it is the largest free clinic in the United States. With an emphasis on primary care, the clinic provides services that span all ages and needs, including prenatal, pediatric preventive, and homeless healthcare. To be eligible for services at the Venice Family Clinic, a person must earn less than 200 percent of the federal poverty level and have no private health insurance. MediCal and Medicare are accepted. More than 22,000 patients visit the clinic annually.

● Of these, 77 percent belong to a minority group, 75 percent have no health insurance, and 70 percent live below the poverty level.

The clinic provides a continuum of care, thanks to partnerships with local hospitals, private labs, pharmaceutical companies, and volunteers. The combined resources of these entities contribute in-kind services that surpass $8 million in value annually. Specialty care is provided through a network of volunteer physicians located in the community and through the Harbor-UCLA Medical Center, the nearest county hospital. HIV/AIDS treatment and chronic disease management, with a focus on diabetes and asthma, are provided. Consultation is available for HIV/AIDS through Cedars-Sinai Medical Center, and volunteer specialists are available for chronic disease management programs. The clinic offers a highly regarded training venue for the hospitals and UCLA, with 33 programs in medicine, mental health, social work, nursing, pharmacy, public health, health administration, and integrative medicine.

In 1994, Elizabeth Benson Forer, MSW, MPH, became the chief executive officer of the Venice Family Clinic. She arrived in Los Angeles from New York City, where she worked at a community health center in East Harlem. Her involvement with the center began as an intern during her studies at Columbia University, and she eventually worked her way to become executive director. Based on her personal experiences at both community health centers and free clinics, she notes that the main difference between the two is the free aspect. Community health centers, as government grantees, must charge a sliding-fee scale for services provided to uninsured patients and are required to bill for their services. Free clinics ask patients for donations but do not bill them, avoiding paperwork and relying instead on donated services and fundraising. Community outreach and community development are fundamental priorities at free clinics. They are the last resort for medically indigent populations who cannot find healthcare anywhere else.

●

Of [22,000 patients annually] 77 percent belong to a minority group, 75 percent have no health insurance, and 70 percent live below the poverty level.

When Forer arrived at the Venice Family Clinic, it was already the largest free clinic in the country and had a well-established volunteer base and support system. She was fortunate to inherit a dedicated fundraiser in the late Irma Colen. Thanks to Colen, the Venice Family Clinic now boasts a premier fundraising vehicle, the Venice Art Walk, held each spring along Venice's famed ocean promenade. The highlight of the art walk, and the key to fundraising for the clinic, is the art auction of donated works by well-known artists. Colen also created the Silver Circle, which raises large individual contributions each year through none-too-subtle peer pressure. Forer's role is to cultivate this growing circle through personal contact and timely stewardship of large gifts.

Forer sometimes wonders why board members seem so devoted and generous to the clinic, and through gentle probing, she has discovered that these individuals almost always have endured a family health crisis that marked their lives. Growing up in Chicago, Colen was hospitalized as a teenager in a charity hospital for rheumatic fever when her family could not afford private healthcare. Motivated by that experience and ready to dial the phone constantly from a desk at the clinic while shuffling through a well-thumbed Rolodex, Colen refused to take no for an answer. Her efforts as a volunteer were prodigious, and the clinic owes her an enormous debt of gratitude.

> Forer sometimes wonders why board members seem so devoted and generous to the clinic, and through gentle probing, she has discovered that these individuals almost always have endured a family health crisis that marked their lives.

Other vehicles also help the clinic survive and prosper. The clinic's board of directors is critical in this effort. The wide circle of physicians who receive their training at the clinic and who stay to practice in nearby hospitals are usually happy to offer assistance when called upon. Also key are relationships with government officials, which have been built painstakingly over time. In a stroke of good fortune, Rep. Jane Harman represents in Congress much of the area served by the Venice Family Clinic (Henry Waxman and Diane Watson represent other parts of the clinic area). Harman's devotion comes, in part, because her own physician father volunteered at the clinic.

Forer, along with board members, staff, and volunteers, shrewdly cultivates the nexus of city, county, state, and federal governments, reaching out to individual politicians as well as to key agencies involved with healthcare.   ●   If she encounters resistance at one level, she does not hesitate to reach out to another in order to influence positive decisions. Her ability to identify and continually add people in the Venice Family Clinic network has created supporters in many different venues. By having converts at the highest levels of government, the clinic has helped save itself from many reversals and has helped keep the county health system from collapsing. This work has enabled the clinic to continue pursuing its fundamental mission, which is to provide access to quality healthcare for low-income, uninsured populations.

●

If [Forer] encounters resistance at one level, she does not hesitate to reach out to another in order to influence positive decisions.

A year after Forer arrived in Venice, she faced her biggest challenge. In 1995, the county health system was collapsing and two county facilities located near the clinic were going to close. The clinic sought to take over these two county clinics. However, already stretched beyond its resources, the clinic lacked space to handle the anticipated increase in demand for services once the county clinics closed. Finding the funds necessary to continue providing services at the county clinics was one challenge; incorporating the county sites into the clinic's structure was an entirely different one. As it turned out, rescuing the county clinics opened the staff, both old and new, to change. With the full support of medical director Susan Fleischman, Forer gained the momentum she needed in order to overcome staff inertia about improving outreach and aligning services. Staffing and medical issues could be addressed in new ways as the clinic doubled in size.

Fortunately for Forer, the threatened demise of the county clinics came after she had already served one year at the clinic. This gave her time to build relationships and knowledge of the clinic and the community. During that first year, she also attended a Robert Wood Johnson seminar on reengineering in healthcare. She began to consider changes that she wanted to make at the clinic, and the knowledge she gained at the seminar helped her shepherd a smooth transition for the county clinics. Instead of the incremental changes for the clinic she had considered during the seminar, she realized she could think big and create momentum for wholesale change. She offered her staff a chance for adventure and, with Fleischman on board, was delighted they were up to the task.

As the two county health clinics joined the Venice Family Clinic, Forer focused on improving primary care preventive services. Because they belong to the community they serve, the clinic staff knew instinctively that treating illness could not alone drive quality healthcare. Children free of ear infections still struggle in school, obese children still struggle to exercise in unsafe neighborhoods, and children treated time after time for asthma still return to apartments above dry cleaners. Over the next decade, in a departure from an exclusive focus on primary care, the staff promoted reading readiness in children by distributing free books to parents, encouraged obese children to exercise with free jump ropes, and advocated for affordable community housing with allergen-free bedrooms. ● Forer pointed out that children sleep better when they read happily at home and school and when they can play safely. Under her direction, the clinic began to monitor its programs to judge whether they helped prevent the conditions that led to illness. This evaluation system continues to help the clinic improve the health of the entire population it serves. This effort also culminated in the creation of the Simms/Mann Health and Wellness Center — the nation's first health, wellness, and integrative medicine program provided by a free clinic.

●

Forer pointed out that children sleep better when they read happily at home and school and when they can play safely.

Forer likes to compare the sudden expansion of the Venice Family Clinic with the children's story *Stone Soup.* In that story, an entrepreneurial homeless man sets a cauldron of water over a roaring fire on a winter's night and adds one stone. When asked by people passing by what he is doing, he replies that he is making stone soup and invites each person to add just one thing of their own — a carrot, a piece of celery, an onion, a potato. Soon the soup becomes a rich and delicious broth that can be shared by all who had contributed. At the Venice Family Clinic, hospitals, community members, volunteers, and patients are all asked to donate something, resulting in the creation of wonderful healthcare services. ✷

Lessons Learned

$\mathcal{G}$eiger would be the first to admit how surprised he was when the federal government responded so rapidly to his suggestions that community health centers be opened. ● Had Sanford Kravitz at the OEO not countered Geiger's request for a small study by upping the ante, the centers at Columbia Point and Mound Bayou may never have been established. The jump-start provided unexpectedly by the OEO enabled Geiger and Tufts to implement community health centers straight away, avoiding the usual tiring battle with bureaucracy.

> ●
>
> Had Sanford Kravitz not countered Geiger's request for a small study by upping the ante, the centers at Columbia Point and Mound Bayou may never have been established.

Like Geiger, Forer seized the moment and incorporated two threatened county clinics, vastly expanding her clinic's facilities, staff, and services. Not satisfied with expansion alone, she refocused the mission of her clinic by offering innovative preventive services. By doing so, the low-income, uninsured populations of western Los Angeles continue to benefit from her vision and leadership.

The lessons learned from Geiger and Forer can be categorized into four basic categories.

The Role of Public Health in Health Policy

Geiger's concept of health centers in the United States benefited from successful models in South Africa that he knew well. His models for areas that had been previously poorly served empowered communities to take ownership of their own healthcare and to focus relentlessly on primary care preventive services. By offering population-based preventive health services, the centers created not just clinical success but environmental improvement, nutritional stability, and new opportunities for employment and local leadership.

Similarly, and because they belong to the community they serve, the staff members of the Venice Family Clinic knew instinctively that treating illness alone could not drive quality healthcare. Forer set about to improve and expand the preventive health services offered at the clinic, leading to programs that focus on literacy, obesity prevention, and improved housing conditions for the population it serves.

Sound Policy Analysis in Public Health Practice

Because of his firsthand exposure to and involvement with the Kark clinics in South Africa, Geiger was able to frame the issue of community health centers so cogently that he quickly won critical backing from key decision-makers at Tufts Medical School and in government. To provide the evidence that the community health center model is working, laws have been enacted over the years requiring centers to conduct assessments of the health status of their target population every two years. ● Since the creation of the first centers, at least 60 independent studies have documented that community health centers offer superior quality in primary care. However, Geiger admits that had a skilled epidemiologist been recruited earlier on, processes could have been fine-tuned faster.

Under Forer's direction, the Venice Family Clinic began to monitor its programs in order to judge whether they helped prevent the conditions that led to illness. This evaluation system continues to help the clinic improve the health of the entire population that it serves. This effort also culminated in the creation of the Simms/Mann Health and Wellness Center — the nation's first health, wellness, and integrative medicine program provided by a free clinic.

The Role of Individuals

Geiger's vision and leadership helped create the community health center movement. While a bit of luck also played a role,

●

Since the creation of the first centers, at least 60 independent studies have documented that community health centers offer superior quality in primary care.

the movement would not have been possible without his tenacity and well-timed advocacy. As a servant leader, he demonstrated many key competencies of public health leadership, above all by honoring the community, nurturing the spirit, and communicating succinctly.

● Similarly, the Venice Family Clinic proves how the power of an idea, when backed by volunteers and community hospitals, can change lives in remarkable ways. More importantly, Forer forsook incremental change at a critical juncture in the clinic's history, inviting her staff to join an adventure and rethink primary care approaches. That adventure created momentum for change on a large scale.

> ●
> The Venice Family Clinic proves how the power of an idea, when backed by volunteers and community hospitals, can change lives in remarkable ways.

Advocacy for Public Health Policy

The community health center movement benefited from President Johnson's War on Poverty, which had just been well-funded by Congress, and from the support of eager advocates working in federal agencies. Geiger knew the rules. Most importantly, he knew that Mississippi's governor could not veto a center run by Tufts in Mound Bayou. He understood that the political will in Washington, D.C., was changing rapidly, and he was able to find like-minded supporters within government who helped make his vision a reality.

Forer's challenge is that she, and her committed staff and supporters, must ceaselessly cultivate funders, government agencies, legislators at all levels of government, and partners to keep the clinic functioning. If she encounters resistance at one level, she does not hesitate to reach out to another to influence positive decisions. Advocacy efforts on behalf of the clinic are constant. By engaging the community in the clinic's survival, Forer helps the community be in control of its own health services — the goal of the community health center movement.

Leadership in health policy sometimes happens in mysterious ways. Although the OEO stunned Geiger with the speed of its funding, he accepted the challenge to create community health centers immediately in such disparate communities as Columbia Point and Mound Bayou. The sudden demise of two county health clinics stunned Forer, but she, nonetheless, turned a potential disaster into an opportunity to effect wholesale change in her free clinic. Both Geiger and Forer forged new paths through uncharted territories, providing access to vital health services to those who had never had it before. ❁ ❁

References

1. U.S. Bureau of the Census. Washington, D.C.: Current population survey, annual social and economic supplements [cited 2006 Oct 1]. Poverty and Health Statistics Branch/HHES Division. Available from: http://www.census.gov/hhes/www/poverty/histpov/hstpov2.html.

2. National Center for Health Statistics. Health, United States, 2006 with chart book on trends in the health of Americans. 2006. table 22: infant mortality rates, fetal mortality rates and prenatal mortality rates, according to race: United States, selected years 1950-2003 [cited 2006 Oct 1]. Available from: http://www.cdc.gov/nchs/data/hus/hus06.pdf#page=183. pp. 166.

3. Almond DV, Chay KY, Greenstone M. Civil rights, the war on poverty and black-white convergence in infant mortality in Mississippi. 2003 Nov [cited 2006 Oct 1]. Available from: http://elsa.berkeley.edu/~kenchay/ftp/binresp/working_paper/mississippi.pdf.

4. Almond DV, Chay KY, Greenstone M. Civil rights, the war on poverty and black-white convergence in infant mortality in Mississippi. 2003 Nov [cited 2006 Oct 1]. Available from: http://elsa.berkeley.edu/~kenchay/ftp/binresp/working_paper/mississippi.pdf.

5. Almond DV, Chay KY, Greenstone M. Civil rights, the war on poverty and black-white convergence in infant mortality in Mississippi. 2003 Nov [cited 2006 Oct 1]. Available from: http://elsa.berkeley.edu/~kenchay/ftp/binresp/working_paper/mississippi.pdf.

Chapter 2. **Righting Wrongs:**
            Creating Insurance Options for
            Underserved Populations

Introduction

*H*ealth insurance may be the most pressing issue facing
the United States healthcare system in the early 21st century.
Those who have health insurance complain of high co-payments,
confusing claims processes, and impersonal bureaucracy. Those
without it often ignore or put off medical care until they are in
a state of crisis and need more intensive and costly interventions.
Not having health insurance or being underinsured (that is, having
inadequate coverage in relation to healthcare needs) carries significant consequences. Uninsured people are significantly more likely
to delay or forego needed care, thereby increasing the risk of
serious and chronic diseases, unmanaged care, premature disability,
and death.[1] ● One study has shown that the lack of health
insurance results in a 25 percent increase in the risk of death.[2]

● One study has
shown that the
lack of health
insurance results
in a 25 percent
increase in the
risk of death.

Being uninsured also has negative implications for communities.
Widespread lack of coverage is associated with family economic
hardship; in fact, 54.5 percent of all bankruptcies in the United
States are associated with economic hardships caused by illness.[3]
The lack of coverage also causes substantial financial losses for
healthcare institutions on which the entire community depends,
as well as a general weakening of economic productivity.[4]
Frighteningly, as much as a third of the population is without
coverage in some U.S. communities.

The United States is the only nation with a high-income economy
that does not guarantee at least some level of health insurance
coverage as a basic benefit to its citizens.[5] In 2007, some 47
million U.S. residents (including 8.7 million children) were
uninsured.[6] The uninsured were disproportionately members of
low-income working families (family income at or below 200

percent of the federal poverty level), and members of racial and ethnic minority groups were without coverage for at least some portion of the year. Furthermore, an eroding voluntary employer-sponsored system and seriously limited governmental programs for the under-65 population mean that over a two-year period, an estimated one in three Americans will experience some length of time without coverage.

The debate over national health reform began more than a century ago in the United States, when other nations with comparable political and economic structures moved to guarantee some level of coverage for virtually their entire populations. In the U.S., however, both healthcare and health insurance coverage remain firmly entrenched as market goods and services, with access heavily determined by the economic and social circumstances of individual families.

The U.S. debate over national health reform has flared up with regularity, typically in connection with a major, action-forcing event. The need to insure American workers was propelled during World War II, when the War Labor Board gave employers the green light to provide their workers with tax-exempt employer-sponsored coverage (a major reform made permanent as part of the federal tax code in 1952). A similar seminal event was the 1964 election of President Lyndon B. Johnson, who had campaigned on a platform of national health reform for the elderly, a group which had been left out of the reforms that had reached the work force. His election resulted in the enactment of Medicare and Medicaid, which today insure more than 100 million Americans.

Although the employer-sponsored coverage system shows enormous signs of strains and erosion, no subsequent event has galvanized a new phase of reform. The 1965 enactments of Medicare and Medicaid stand as watershed events in U.S. social policy that have not been repeated. In the intervening 40-some years, both programs have been strengthened and expanded. In 1997, for example, Congress enacted a modest supplement, the State Children's Health Insurance Program (SCHIP), to further broaden Medicaid's reach to children. Today, Medicare covers more than 45 million older people and certain workers with disabilities. Medicaid, the largest of all U.S. health insurance programs, covered nearly 60 million individuals in 2006, including more than 25 million children; SCHIP covered an additional four million children that year.

The history of health reform in the United States is replete with political failure. President Franklin D. Roosevelt decided not to even propose health reform as part of the 1935 Social Security Act in order to save the rest of the legislation. His decision was followed by a succession of presidential and congressional failures to reach consensus on the issue', culminating in the collapse of President Bill Clinton's health reform plan in 1994.[8] ● Because fundamental health reform is so difficult to achieve, it is important to understand those cases in which health reform succeeded.

> Because fundamental health reform is so difficult to achieve, it is important to understand those cases in which health reform succeeded.

While the United States still does not guarantee access to coverage for all citizens, the opportunity for achieving political consensus for universal coverage may again be within reach. Rising healthcare costs and increases in the numbers of uninsured and underinsured are driving growing sentiment against the current system. If Congress, the executive branch, and the public are to achieve consensus, they will need to embrace the economic and social benefits that universal coverage would bring. As state budgets have limited funds, the consensus will most likely be at the federal level; and as most people, including political leaders, rate healthcare as only one of many important issues,[9] the clarion call for leadership is needed once again.

The following case studies offer profiles of leaders who answered that call. Rashi Fein, PhD, served in the trenches with distinction for several presidents while universal health insurance was debated. He was present at the creation of Medicare and Medicaid, the two major federal health insurance programs, and helped implement both. This work paved the way for future political leaders, such as Assemblyman Richard Gottfried of New York, who continues to lead efforts in his state to expand healthcare coverage for children. ❁

National Case Study

Rashi Fein and the Creation of Medicare and Medicaid

*D*r. Rashi Fein came to the world of health policy purely by accident. In searching for a dissertation topic while a doctoral student in political economy at Johns Hopkins University, Fein was introduced by a fellow student to her husband, Dr. E. F. Penrose. A professor of economic geography, Penrose had published a book on health insurance at a time when Gov. Earl Warren of California was proposing universal health insurance in his state. In 1949, Penrose encouraged Fein to focus his disser- tation on healthcare because so little had been written in that field. Fein's faculty arranged a one-year fellowship for him in the History of Medicine Department at the Johns Hopkins School of Hygiene and Public Health. However, given his unusual academic background and the school's confusion over what to do with an economist, he spent the year reading medical journals in the library.

Rashi Fein, PhD

Ultimately, Fein conceptualized a dissertation topic focusing on physician payment. To do so, he sought out William Weinfeld at the U.S. Department of Commerce, the author of an issue of the *Survey of Current Business* that culled government statistics and data from private surveys on the income of physicians, dentists, and lawyers. The survey showed stable income for lawyers, along with rising income for doctors.

Fein believed that Weinfeld had much more data to share. In an era before photocopiers and the Internet, Fein had to go to lengths to borrow the files. His request was denied by the American Medical Association, whose members collaborated with the Commerce Department in the data collection effort, and whose permission was essential. This put a halt to Fein's dissertation topic, but Weinfeld invited him to serve on President

Harry S. Truman's newly formed Commission on the Health Needs of the Nation, established in 1951. Fein, who would begin teaching that fall in the Department of Economics at the University of North Carolina (UNC) Chapel Hill, agreed to a nine-month stint. Suddenly, Fein found himself in the world of health policy.

Fein realized that his role on the presidential commission would allow him to request any data available. Naturally, he first approached the Department of Commerce to request the income data for doctors that had been denied to him. At the commission, and while he worked with five or six others on manpower issues, he had those Department of Commerce files handy on his desk. Once he reached UNC at Chapel Hill, however, his focus shifted to the local aspects of medicine and economics, and he decided not to pursue his original topic. Instead, for his dissertation he researched factors that influence general practitioners in North Carolina — how they choose their place to practice and the policy implications.

Although Fein's work at the commission focused on manpower issues, the commission's head of research, Lester Breslow, really wanted to organize a system that would be effective and more sensible for the delivery of healthcare. Through his efforts, the commission proposed organizing care around prepaid group practice. However, it did not deal with the issue of how to pay for universal health insurance.

Once he started to teach economics at UNC at Chapel Hill in 1952, Fein kept his hand in healthcare by working part time in the program planning section of the Division of Health Affairs as UNC moved from a two-year to a four-year School of Medicine, and opened a School of Dentistry, a School of Nursing and a School of Pharmacy. These schools were in addition to the School of Public Health that had been established in 1939. Funded by the Rockefeller Foundation, the planning section had a limited lifespan, and when the funding expired, Fein turned to full-time teaching in the department of economics.

Several years later, through his UNC colleagues Gordon Blackwell and Rupert Vance, Fein met Jack Ewalt of Harvard University, head of the Joint Commission on Mental Illness and Health. Ewalt encouraged Fein to write a book on the economics of mental illness. Fein accepted $400 a month to write the book and decided to concentrate not merely on the costs of treatment in mental hospitals but also on the resulting loss of productivity in the American economy. After consulting with Paul Samuelson and Robert Solow at the Massachusetts Institute of Technology, among others, Fein pioneered the concept of direct and indirect cost allocation, something now taken for granted in economics. The costs of treatment were direct costs; the loss of production, indirect costs. Basic Books published the book in 1958, earning Fein a reputation as an expert in the field of health economics.

During the Kennedy administration, Fein served on the Council of Economic Advisors under Walter Heller. He had spent the summer before the 1960 election in the library at Williams College researching the literature on how to quantify the value of what a human being can produce. After the election and Kennedy's inaugural address, he was drawn to Washington. At the intervention of friends, he was offered a job at the council to deal with what Fein calls the "do good" programs — health, education, Social Security, welfare, and manpower retraining. As he says,

●   "It was put to me that we were working for a president who thinks economics has something to say about everything." On the first day, he walked into the chairman's office and Heller said, "Go to it." Fein asked, "What is *it*?" Heller replied, "I don't know; you know this field better than I." Fein looks back on the years at the council as having been the highlight of his career.

Right from the start, Fein used his status on the Council of Economic Advisors to extend lunch invitations to long-serving civil servants at the Department of Health, Education and Welfare (HEW, now known as the Department of Health and Human Services, or HHS) to seek their expertise. A colleague advised him that they would always accept his invitations because

> ●
>
> "It was put to me that we were working for a president who thinks economics has something to say about everything."

they were eager to connect with someone whose ideas might coincide with their own, after feeling suppressed during the Eisenhower years. Over the course of months, Fein came to know HEW and the experts who worked there. He met economists who knew more about education and Social Security than he did. He became very impressed with the knowledge level of these hard-working civil servants, something he says was hard for an academic to admit.

Since 1958, there had been an effort to enact what later came to be called Medicare Part A, social insurance focused on hospital care. It failed year after year to get out of committee. Conservative members of the House and Senate (including Wilbur Mills, the legendary chairman of the House Ways and Means Committee) kept it bottled up until after the 1964 Johnson landslide.   ●   Half of the elderly population at the time did not have health insurance. Most were retired and had not brought their employer-provided health insurance with them into retirement. This was not a traditional retirement benefit, although the automobile industry was soon to change that, following the example of universities and city, county, and state governments. The problem was so severe that two parties suffered from it — the elderly without health insurance and the hospitals that took care of them. Doctors in private practice did not suffer in equal measure, because they could refuse patients while hospitals could not.

●

Half of the elderly population at the time did not have health insurance.

After the Democratic sweep in the 1958 congressional elections, the health insurance effort gathered steam, with suggestions that hospital coverage for the elderly be a compulsory part of Social Security. However, what became known as Medicare Part A did not gain enough traction for passage. In 1963, President John F. Kennedy mounted another major push, but his speech before a big rally in Madison Square Garden fell flat. Two weeks later, the American Medical Association (AMA) rented Madison Square Garden for a counter rally. The speech by the president of AMA managed to forestall again what was called the "juggernaut of oppressive big government."

Fein continued to reach out to HEW during his tenure on the Council of Economic Advisors, and he continued to contribute to the health section in the president's annual Economic Report. He addressed issues of health insurance for the elderly, as well as medication and racial discrimination. However, it was Wilbur Cohen, an originator of the Social Security Act and an assistant secretary at HEW under Kennedy, who was the lead administration contact in the development of legislation and strategy to incorporate medical care for the elderly as part of social insurance.

In the 1960s, healthcare costs were five percent of the gross domestic product, compared with 14 percent or more today. Although the American Hospital Association (AHA) and even BlueCross BlueShield favored health insurance for the elderly sponsored through Social Security, the AMA fought it bitterly, positing that big government would target doctors next. Today, "experience rating" is common in health insurance; this means that people pay different premiums based on differences in their demographics, past healthcare utilization, medical status, and other factors. ● In the early 1960s, however, everyone paid fixed premiums through community rating and the uninsured elderly were driving up the cost of hospital insurance for everyone. In 1964, a major turning point occurred with the election of Lyndon B. Johnson. President Johnson's promise of social reform, most notably Medicare and federal aid to education, triumphed over Barry Goldwater's "alternatives of state, local, and private initiative."[10]

●

In the early 1960s, however, everyone paid fixed premiums through community rating and the uninsured elderly were driving up the cost of hospital insurance for everyone.

To Fein, Medicare's popularity and survival is founded on its universality — every person over 65 is a beneficiary, the janitor as well as the millionaire. Cuts would affect everyone, as they would with Social Security. Medicare has escaped elimination time and time again because it is universal. Although Medicare was meant to be a building block toward national health insurance, that goal has yet to be achieved. Critics point especially to two shortcomings — money is spent unnecessarily because of lax regulation and poor accountability, with a focus on paying bills rather than ensuring quality of care. Medicare and Medicaid created a huge industry of subcontractors who process paperwork rather than measure quality and health outcomes.

After Kennedy's assassination, Johnson used the martyred president as a rallying cry for the advancement of domestic legislation. It helped that his landslide victory in 1964 produced dramatic gains for Democrats in Congress. By the end of 1965, Congress passed Medicare and Medicaid, along with regional medical programs and aid to medical schools. Meanwhile, pleased with the work he had performed for Kennedy, Fein left the council in early 1963 to join the Brookings Institution, although he continued with part-time government work on weekends. At Brookings, he began to write a book about physician shortages.

> "Men were dumb and gave women the statistician jobs while reserving policy for themselves, not understanding that she who controls the data is very influential on policy."
>
>

Following the dramatic shift of the 1964 election, Cohen and Mills jointly planned a voluntary, premium-based Medicare Part B, as well as Part A, for the non-elderly disabled. They approached Johnson for an additional $500 million, and he agreed. Today, although Part B is still voluntary, beneficiaries have to opt out rather than opt in. From the start, Part B gained 98 percent participation. Since 2003, Medicare also has a premium-based Part D, the outpatient prescription drug benefit passed by a Republican-controlled Congress. Fein points out how fortunate Medicare was to have Dorothy Rice as its first chief statistician. Fein says, "Men were dumb and gave women the statistician jobs while reserving policy for themselves, not understanding that she who controls the data is very influential on policy."

Fein remembers a conversation he had with Kermit Gordon, president of the Brookings Institution, in the elevator one Sunday evening during the Medicare negotiations on regulations and definitions of "costs" eligible for reimbursement. Reformers were criticizing Johnson for giving away too much to hospitals, but the AMA and AHA lobbying against the legislation were effective. Fein remembers Gordon saying, "I spent the weekend with the American Hospital Association, and I feel that between the

AHA and Fort Knox, there stands a lonely soul, Kermit Gordon, guarding the gold."

During the Johnson administration, Fein chaired the President's Medicaid Advisory Committee. He knew all the players involved with the Medicare and Medicaid Acts and, in his advisory role at the Brookings Institution, helped in the implementation of these large federal healthcare programs. A key difference between a Medicaid recipient and a Medicare beneficiary is that the former must approach his or her home county, reapply each year for benefits, and offer proof of need. The bureaucratic structure can often be daunting to the uninitiated. As structured during the Johnson administration, the federal government pays half of Medicaid costs on average, and states and localities pay the other half and administer the program through local social service agencies. Unlike Medicare, Medicaid is an income-eligible program.

The vital role played by Medicare in desegregating the South has been forgotten, Fein believes. But he lived through its early implementation and can attest that the two greatest challenges were convincing doctors to sign up and desegregating hospitals.
●   The administration made a conscious, deliberate decision that no federal money would go to a segregated institution.

When Medicare began on July 1, 1966, there were fears that the elderly would overrun hospitals, having postponed surgeries until the program began. Hospitals were barely able to handle that spurt in demand, but over the years, the Medicare program has proved to be a boon to hospital expansion, guaranteeing low-cost construction loans that make banks secure in their lending and giving grants for research facilities that are, in effect, cost-free.

Another legacy of Medicare, improved quality of care, has not come without rising healthcare costs. Even during the Johnson administration, within two years of the Medicare and Medicaid passage, a task force was convened to address the issue of rapidly rising healthcare costs. While the effects of Medicare's universal health insurance to the elderly have been salutary, inflated

●

The administration made a conscious, deliberate decision that no federal money would go to a segregated institution.

healthcare costs are also a legacy. With the hospital expansion that accompanied Medicare, spending has been more on acute care than on prevention. Furthermore, Medicare spending has become a large component of national health spending and also a major segment of the federal budget.[11] The estimated net federal spending on Medicare is expected to grow to $444 billion in 2010.[12]

In 1980, Fein gave the commencement address at the University of Michigan's School of Medicine, with the theme that the physicians and faculty should thank Medicare. This was not because Medicare had raised their incomes (which it had, he pointed out), but because advances in medicine had increased the cost of medical care. Without Medicare, physicians would face patients on a daily basis for whom they knew what to do but wouldn't be able to do it. They would have to deny care that patients couldn't afford and ration care on the basis of income. He also pointed out that Medicare helped break the barriers of segregation in American society.

Fein's career exemplifies how public health policy often gets made through serendipity.

● Fein's career exemplifies how public health policy often gets made through serendipity. When he arrived at Brookings in 1963, Fein intended to write about the economics of education. Yet, after attending a conference where he heard physicians make many misstatements about health manpower, he decided to write about physician shortages instead, which kept his hand in the thick of public health policy. Were it not for his initial choice of a dissertation topic, he likely would never have become a health economist in the first place. Fortunately, his career path has led others to follow his example and to look for ways to expand health insurance coverage for all populations.

The case study that follows explores the role of a state legislator, with neither a medical nor public health background, who has been deeply committed to expanding access to care and coverage for children. ❁

Local Case Study

Richard Gottfried and SCHIP in New York

Richard Gottfried, JD

Since 1970 when he was first elected while still a law student at Columbia University, Richard Gottfried has served his New York State Assembly district, covering the Manhattan neighborhoods of Chelsea, Hell's Kitchen, Midtown, parts of Murray Hill, and the Lincoln Center area. As chairman of the Assembly Committee on Health since May 1987, he was instrumental in shaping a precursor to SCHIP in New York. This program, called Child Health Plus, was initiated in 1991, and his involvement with health coverage for children deepened over time. Most significantly, he played a key role in expanding and refining New York State's program through additional legislation in 1998 and 2002, after Congress enacted SCHIP in 1997. These years coincided with the re-election of New York's Republican governor, George Pataki, which turned out to be a critical factor in Gottfried's ability to move the legislation through to passage.

New York has always led the nation in shaping public health policy on access to care, with Medicaid in New York being more generous than in any other state. Although New York modeled its 1991 child health insurance program on a similar program already enacted in Minnesota, the New York program still led the nation in many ways. Gottfried recalls the health commissioner, Dr. David Axelrod, advocating for a program that would cover both outpatient and inpatient care for a limited low-income population with a sliding-scale premium. Axelrod succeeded at getting Gov. Mario Cuomo to insert the proposal in his budget. However, Gottfried immediately heard from advocacy groups that wanted to change the proposal to one that would cover only outpatient care, with no premium for low-income parents, and a sliding-scale premium for moderate-income parents. These advocates, led by Dr. Louis Z. Cooper, then head of the state chapter of the American Academy of Pediatrics, argued that New York had a pre-existing "bad debt and charity care" program that already partly reimbursed hospitals for providing inpatient services for low-income patients, including children. He argued that the most important services for most children are primary and preventive care, requiring increased resources for outpatient care. Concentrating on outpatient care alone would also lower overall costs, making it possible to enroll many more children without resorting to premiums.

Remarkably, this revised child health insurance plan sailed through the legislature, which enacted it in the first go-around. In Gottfried's experience, this was a rare, swift victory for a major policy initiative, especially astonishing in 1991 as revenue short-falls were beginning to constrain growth in New York's budget. A key factor was that Cuomo, at Axelrod's urging, had made child health insurance one of his priorities in negotiations over renewal of the state's hospital reimbursement legislation.

The New York Child Health Plus program at first limited participation to both family income status and age — children 12 years of age and under. This age limit conveniently avoided the issue of reproductive care. While Gottfried believed that the program should be more comprehensive to include dental and vision care, among other services, he accepted the initial limits in the interest of enactment.   ●   He knew that limiting costs would be a key consideration in passage and believed that the program could be expanded in the future, and it was. The New York Legislature expanded the program in small ways every two years, raising either the age limit or family-income level and introducing new services.

●

He knew that limiting costs would be a key consideration in passage and believed that the program could be expanded in the future, and it was.

Gottfried says, "In 1997, Congress, in one of the most intelligent, farsighted things I've seen them do in almost a generation, targeted a big increase in tobacco-tax money for child health insurance programs to be run by the states." Congress based its SCHIP program on New York State's Child Health Plus and programs in several other states, giving latitude to states to devise their own programs within broad federal guidelines to qualify for federal matching funds. New York qualified for a 65 percent match, considerably more than the state's 50 percent Medicaid match, giving a boost to advocates for expanding Child Health Plus.

As chairman of the Assembly Committee on Health, Gottfried made child health insurance a top priority on the Assembly's agenda. Had he not done that, many other worthy causes may have pushed it aside. Again in 1998, with the new SCHIP funding available, he led the charge for a major expansion of Child Health Plus and encouraged the advocacy community to be expansive in its proposals. The Children's Defense Fund and the Local 1199 Health Care Workers Union were major contributors to overcoming Pataki's reluctance to expand the program. Although the governor received credit for proposing universal child health insurance in his State of the State speech that year, his actual proposal barely expanded benefits and required that all but the lowest income level buy into the program. In effect, the governor's proposal did not expand eligibility for Child Health Plus and offered only a limited expansion of benefits. This became a major budget disagreement between the Assembly and the governor. However, since the governor was seeking re-election and desired Local 1199's support, the Assembly had a strong hand and won the battle.

For Gottfried, access to care and coverage are not just health issues. They are also increasingly economic and social justice issues. Employer-based health insurance, when it is available, has moved toward high-deductible, low-coverage insurance policies that can be devastating for low-income people. He says, "To me, the fight for affordable health coverage, and particularly for publicly sponsored health coverage with broad-based public financing, is an important part of the effort to stem the radical shift in wealth going on in this country, away from working people toward the upper slice of society." Gottfried remains concerned that Child Health Plus is still a means-tested program, requiring proof of eligibility — how old you are, how poor your parents are — every year. By comparison, as he points out, no senior is ineligible for Medicare because of wealth, no child is ineligible for public elementary or secondary school, and no proof is required every year for either.   ● According to Gottfried, bureaucratic enrollment obstacles in all of New York's public health coverage programs keep at least 1.4 million eligible New Yorkers from enrolling every year.

●

According to Gottfried, bureaucratic enrollment obstacles in all of New York's public health coverage programs keep at least 1.4 million eligible New Yorkers from enrolling every year.

In 2002, which was another re-election year for a governor still anxious to gain the support of Local 1199, Gottfried's legislative focus in the Assembly Committee on Health became bureaucratic obstacles to enrollment, known as "simplification." The Assembly again played a strong hand and won many, but not all, of its recommendations. Provisions were enacted for easing re-enrollment, particularly for Child Health Plus. Opponents preyed on fears that ineligible participants would sneak into the program as a result of lax enforcement and raise costs. However, after the Sept. 11, 2001, tragedy, New York created a Disaster Relief Medicaid program that enrolled every applicant without proof of eligibility. This was a response to the destruction of the central computer link for the Medicaid system in New York City and of the region caused by the collapse of a building at the World Trade Towers site. New York's Medicaid rolls bumped up dramatically as a result. But in the years since then, enrollment has remained at the post-9/11 level. A fair conclusion would be that reduced barriers to access ushered many more eligible participants into the program but that fraud was not a factor.

In 2007, Gottfried was delighted to see two key proposals included in Gov. Eliot Spitzer's budget: a dramatic increase in the income-eligibility level for the Child Health Plus program (from 250 percent to 400 percent of the federal poverty level) and the Assembly's proposals for simplifying re-enrollment in Child Health Plus and Medicaid. Both were approved by the Legislature with virtually no opposition or change.

Gottfried has seen New York's Child Health Plus program become what he originally envisioned. The program has provided thousands of children with access to preventive and acute health-care. It has helped provide stability for community health centers, safety net hospitals, and other healthcare providers. Politically, it has helped build public acceptance for the concept of publicly sponsored health coverage and, in so doing, has helped expand health coverage for other populations in New York. Gottfried says, ● "Some people do crossword puzzles for a hobby, but I draft bills." A modest man, he can nonetheless take pride in his legislative accomplishments.

●

"Some people do crossword puzzles for a hobby, but I draft bills."

Gottfried notes that he relies on well-informed advocacy groups to help him shape his healthcare agenda. He has found that the notes he takes when he meets with advocates are often trans-formed, in some cases verbatim, into the legislation he drafts and proposes. Being an effective listener is not enough, however. Persuasion is essential in driving new legislation forward. He has been remarkably successful at gaining the attention of the speaker of the Assembly — a powerful force in New York politics — and in persuading his fellow Assembly members that his proposals deserve their votes of approval. Gottfried is also guided by his strong notion of social equity. He says, "Health professionals find that when they talk to people in my line of work, they are eagerly listened to, particularly by someone like me who is basically a lay person, as almost all legislators are. Leadership to me means being open to new ideas from people who really know what they are talking about and who share your values, and then doing your utmost to put those ideas into practice." ✸

Lessons Learned

$\mathcal{T}$he stories of Fein and Gottfried demonstrate that champions from fields outside public health, whether from the political or economic fields, are needed in order to push access to care to the top of the policy agenda. There are important lessons to be learned from their examples.

The Role of Public Health in Health Policy

As a health economist in two presidential administrations, Fein had a hand in shaping two major pieces of health coverage that continue to define the U.S. healthcare system. Fein knew that the aspect of universality would protect Medicare in the long term. Because everyone 65 years and older is eligible, regardless of socioeconomic, racial, or ethnic background, the program has been embraced by society despite its limitations. Medicaid has strengthened the nation's safety net for the poor, and even though it has seen many budget cuts, it continues to serve the healthcare needs of underserved populations.

> ● Because everyone 65 years and older is eligible, regardless of socioeconomic, racial, or ethnic background, the program has been embraced by society despite its limitations.

Gottfried views the bureaucracy surrounding enrollment in public health coverage programs as being a major threat to population health. Enrollment requirements keep away nearly one and a half million people who are eligible to participate in these programs. His efforts to simplify enrollment in SCHIP are important drivers of improving access to healthcare.

Sound Policy Analysis in Public Health Practice

Fein used his academic background in economics to help create new health policies that changed American society. At a time when paid fixed premiums (community ratings) were the norm in the health insurance industry, Fein and his colleagues in government and industry could see that the uninsured elderly were driving up the cost of hospital insurance for everyone. The advent of Medicare changed the way the insurance industry functions even today, and it will continue to do so.

Gottfried was influenced by the arguments of Louis Cooper and the New York chapter of the American Academy of Pediatrics when designing the Child Health Plus program. By listening to their analysis of the state's existing charity care programs, Gottfried changed course and refocused the new program on outpatient care, with its emphasis on prevention and wellness, rather than on inpatient services.

The Role of Individuals

By seeking out the advice and expertise of long-serving civil servants, Fein was able to bring important perspective and experience to his role on the Council of Economic Advisors.
● Along the way, he discovered that academics can learn much from civil servants who have become experts in the day-to-day work of policy implementation.

Gottfried used his political position to guarantee and expand health coverage for the most vulnerable population, children. He understood that a governor seeking re-election would want to be seen as an advocate for children and families, and he garnered the support of a powerful union to help secure passage of needed legislation.

Advocacy for Public Health Policy

Both Fein and Gottfried feel that access to health insurance coverage goes beyond health and into economic and social justice. Fein doesn't want current generations to overlook the important role that Medicare played in desegregating the South. Through his efforts, and those of many others, the Johnson administration made the deliberate decision to exclude segregated institutions from receiving federal funds.

●

Along the way, he discovered that academics can learn much from civil servants who have become experts in the day-to-day work of policy implementation.

Gottfried continues to work closely with advocacy groups that help him shape the Assembly agenda. However, he is also guided by his own strong feelings about social equity. He is not content to let his coverage programs become stagnant; ● rather, just as healthcare needs and challenges continue to grow, so must programs that serve those who are at greatest risk for disease and disability.

●

...rather, just as healthcare needs and challenges continue to grow, so must programs that serve those who are at greatest risk for disease and disability.

Fein and Gottfried would agree that universal healthcare coverage is the linchpin for access to healthcare services in this country. Without such coverage, care is intermittent, acute, and not focused on prevention. The importance of health insurance coverage as a public health policy issue resonates with the social justice imperative that lies at the heart of public health. ❋ ❋

References

1. Davis MH, Burner ST. Three decades of Medicare: what the numbers tell us. *Health Affairs*. winter; 14(4): 231-243.
2. Institute of Medicine. Care without coverage: too little, too late. Washington, DC: The National Academies Press; 2002.
3. Himmelstein DU, Warren E, Thorne D, Woolhandler S. MarketWatch: Illness And Injury As Contributors To Bankruptcy. *Health Affairs*. 2005 Feb 2; Suppl Web Exclusives: W5-63-W5-73.
4. Institute of Medicine. Hidden cost, value lost: uninsurance in America. Washington, DC: The National Academies Press; 2003.
5. Battista JR, McCabe J. The case for single payer, universal health care for the United States. Outline of presentation at: The Association of State Green Parties; 1999 Jun 4; Moodus, CT. Available from: http://cthealth.server101.com/the_case_for_universal_health_care_in_the_united_states.htm.
6. Household income rises, poverty rate declines, number of uninsured up. [news release]. Washington, DC: U.S. Census Bureau News. 2007 Aug 28. Available from: http://www.census.gov/PressRelease/www/releases/archives/income_wealth/010583.html.
7. Starr P. The social transformation of American medicine. New York: Basic Books; 1982. pp. 235-290.
8. Skocpol T. Boomerang: Clinton's health security effort and the turn against government in U.S. politics. New York: W.W. Norton & Company; 1996. p. 54.
9. Kaye N, Marchev M, Riley T. Building a pathway to universal coverage: how do we get from here to there? National Academy for State Health Policy. 2002 Nov; 24.
10. Marmor TR. The politics of Medicare. 2nd ed. Hawthorne: Aldine de Gruyter, 2000. p. 45.
11. The Henry J. Kaiser Family Foundation[Home page on the Internet]. Medicare spending and financing. 2005 April [cited 09-12-07]. Available from: http://www.kff.org/medicare/upload/7305.pdf.
12. The Henry J. Kaiser Family Foundation [Home page on the Internet]. Menlo Park (CA): Medicare at a glance. 2007 Feb. [cited 2007 Aug 23]. Available from: http://www.kff.org/medicare/upload/1066-10.pdf.

Chapter 3.   **Leveling the Playing Field:**
             Addressing Health Disparities

Introduction

*E*nsuring the quality and accountability of healthcare to the
entire population — regardless of language, culture, race, or
socioeconomic, educational, and immigration status — is one
of the highest aspirations of any national health system. Despite
noble intentions and dedicated professionals, the U.S. healthcare
system reveals a paradox of values versus economic realities.
Embracing diversity is a core value of the United States, but the
nation's healthcare system has a long history of exclusion and
discrimination based on race, socioeconomic status, and
national origin.   ●   Achieving equality in healthcare poses
enormous challenges, which can be seen clearly in the disparities
that characterize national, state, and community health statistics.

●

Achieving
equality in
healthcare
poses enormous
challenges, which
can be seen clearly
in the disparities
that characterize
national, state,
and community
health statistics.

Healthy People 2010 defines racial health disparities as the "unequal
burden in disease morbidity and mortality rates experienced by
ethnic or racial groups as compared to the dominant group." A
2002 Institute of Medicine report, *Unequal Treatment: Confronting
Racial and Ethnic Disparities in Healthcare*, refines this definition further,
pointing to "differences in the quality of healthcare that are not
due to access-related factors or clinical needs, preferences, or
appropriateness of intervention."[1]

Health disparities reflecting differences tied to socioeconomic
status, race, national origin, and language have been extensively
documented in the United States. Compared with their white
counterparts, minority populations, such as Hispanics, African-
Americans, Asian-Americans, and Native Americans, experience
higher rates of morbidity and mortality at every age.[2] As **Figure 1**
shows, disparities span both health and healthcare, and disparities
can be seen across the spectrum of care, from preventive services
to timely acute care and services for the treatment of chronic
illness and disability.

Figure 1

Health and Healthcare Disparities in the United States

Infant Mortality	African-American, Native American, and Puerto Rican infants have higher death rates than white infants.[3]
Cancer Screening and Management	African-American women are more than twice as likely to die of cervical cancer than are white women, and are more likely to die of breast cancer than are women of any other racial or ethnic group.[4]
Cardiovascular Disease	In 2000, rates of death from diseases of the heart were 29 percent higher among African-American adults than among white adults, and death rates from stroke were 40 percent higher.[5]
Diabetes	In 2000, Native Americans and Alaska Natives were 2.6 times more likely to have diagnosed diabetes compared with non-Hispanic whites; African-Americans were 2.0 times more likely, and Hispanics were 1.9 times more likely.[6]
HIV Infection/ AIDS	Although African-Americans and Hispanics represented only 26 percent of the U.S. population in 2001, they accounted for 66 percent of adult AIDS cases[7] and 82 percent of pediatric AIDS cases reported in the first half of that year.[8]
Immunizations	In 2001, Hispanics and African-Americans aged 65 and older were less likely than non-Hispanic whites to report having received influenza and pneumococcal vaccines.[9]
Hospitalization for Ambulatory Care Sensitive Conditions	Preventable hospitalization rates have been found to be notably higher for African-Americans and Hispanics than for non-Hispanic whites for almost all of the conditions, both for women and men and for all age groups.[10]

There are many reasons for health disparities in the United States. These reasons include lack of access to affordable health insurance coverage and barriers to enrollment in public programs, such as Medicaid or the State Children's Health Insurance Program (SCHIP). They also include low health literacy, which is associated with poverty, limited education, and a lack of health insurance. Other reasons include a healthcare system that is not structured to accommodate a range of beliefs and traditions about health, and healthcare providers whose own cultural beliefs and attitudes, combined with a lack of training in caring for a diverse patient population, exacerbate the problem.[11] All of these factors merge into an intricate systemic problem for public health policy and practice.

Certain civil rights laws, whose purpose is to prevent and remedy discrimination against racial and ethnic minority populations, as well as people with disabilities, have been used as the basis of health policymaking over the years. For example, the landmark Civil Rights Act of 1964, which prohibits discrimination on the basis of race and national origin in federally assisted programs, was applied to all hospitals in 1965 as a condition of participation in Medicare and Medicaid. In addition, all publicly funded health facilities must comply with the accessibility requirements of the Americans With Disabilities Act of 1990. The simple application of law to the healthcare system tends to produce incomplete or partial results, however, because the task involves changing the fundamental nature of how the system interacts with populations at great risk for diminished or inadequate care and services.

It is in this context that public health policy took a seminal turn in the 1990s, embracing disparities in health and healthcare not simply as a legal issue but as a public health issue as well. This embrace coincided with the publication of a series of major reports showing the extent of the disparities problem, and has introduced an era in which the reduction of health disparities is understood to be a central and overarching matter of health and public health policy, not just an issue for civil rights law. The following several studies examining disparities in healthcare have been of particular importance: a 1999 study undertaken by the Agency for Healthcare Research and Quality; a 1999 report issued by the President's Civil Rights Commission; and the Institute of Medicine's 2000 study, *Unequal Treatment*. This study systematically detailed the extent of the disparities problem and found a link between disparities in healthcare and the interaction with patients at the clinical care level.[12]

● In recent years, numerous federal agency initiatives have sought to advance the goal of reducing health disparities. The *Healthy People 2010* initiative of the U.S. Department of Health and Human Services, issued by Surgeon General David Satcher in 2000 (following the precedent set by Surgeon General Julius Richmond in the 1970s), set objectives for health promotion and disease prevention for the nation, with an aim toward eliminating health disparities by the year 2010. As of 2004, 34 states had designated a government entity to address minority health.[13] Furthermore, the reduction of health disparities has become a specific goal of national associations and organizations. Of particular note was an initiative (discontinued by the federal government in 2006) that funded the development of specific healthcare interventions at the nation's community health centers in order to reduce racial, ethnic, and socioeconomic disparities in health status linked to certain chronic diseases. This effort resulted in significant disparities reduction at the clinics at which the effort was funded.[14] Finally, Racial and Ethnic Approaches to Community Health (REACH 2010), an ongoing initiative of the Centers for Disease Control and Prevention, supports community-based projects designed to eliminate disparities and improve outcomes for a variety of diseases among racial and ethnic minorities.[15]

●

In recent years, numerous federal agency initiatives have sought to advance the goal of reducing health disparities.

The national case study that follows examines the work of Nicole Lurie, MD, MSPH, and Thomas Perez, JD, MPP, in overcoming language barriers to healthcare access while they

were colleagues at the U.S. Department of Health and
Human Services from 1999 to 2001. Their research and policy
development led to a presidential executive order known as the
Limited English Proficiency Directive that established guidelines
for the treatment of patients with limited English proficiency in
federally supported healthcare settings. These guidelines, whose
applicability was reaffirmed by the Bush administration in 2003
in slightly modified form, have been widely adopted. At the local
level, reducing health disparities in California's minority communities has been the focus of Dr. Robert Ross, a former public
health officer and, since 2001, the chief executive officer of The
California Endowment. The central grant-making focus of The
Endowment, an independent, nonprofit foundation based in
Los Angeles, is supporting interventions that can be replicated
nationally. ❁

National Case Study

Nicole Lurie, Thomas Perez, and the Limited English Proficiency Directive

*D*uring the final two years of the Clinton administration from 1999 to 2001, Nicole Lurie, MD, MSPH, served as the principal deputy assistant secretary for health at the U.S. Department of Health and Human Services (HHS) Office of Public Health and Science. During that same time span, Thomas Perez, JD, MPP, served as the head of the HHS Office for Civil Rights, whose mission is to ensure compliance with civil rights laws throughout the department.

Nicole Lurie, MD, MSPH

A nationally renowned health services researcher, as well as a medical clinician who has focused her career on questions of health and healthcare inequalities, Lurie had previously been instrumental in the development of Minnesota Care, a comprehensive children's health coverage program. Her role with Minnesota Care had been as an impartial collector of data, amassing data to the point where evidence of disparities became both overwhelming and incontrovertible. As a researcher, Lurie notes, "Without data, it is not possible to know if there are disparities and, just as importantly, whether disparities are being reduced."

Perez had come to the Justice Department's Civil Rights Division in 1989, where he had been involved in numerous civil and criminal matters. However, he had not had occasion to work in the field of healthcare until he arrived at HHS and took the helm of the Office for Civil Rights.

Thomas Perez, JD, MPP

In the spring of 1999, the Clinton administration convened a meeting of the heads of all civil rights offices at the White House, chaired by deputy chief of staff Maria Echeveste. The question for discussion was, assuming that only two years remained for a Democratic administration, could sustainable civil rights initiatives be undertaken to help people?

Perez, who was at the meeting, suggested that the problem of language access be addressed as a basic public health issue. Title VI of the Civil Rights Act obligates government agencies to ensure that people with limited English proficiency have access to all government services at the federal, state, and local levels. Perez says, "This was an example of a crosscutting issue, quite timely and relevant given the changing face of America." Perez also believed that it was the type of initiative that, once put into place, could not easily be repealed by subsequent administrations — given its fundamental importance to healthcare and its importance to basic population health. He saw his role as head of the HHS Office for Civil Rights as shining a light on healthcare, what he calls the forgotten frontier of civil rights.

After the presidential meeting, Perez and Lurie convened a task force that was drawn from across the department and that involved many federal agencies to determine how best to reduce health disparities caused by language barriers. Having been surrounded by lawyers during his years at the Justice Department, Perez loved the eclectic nature of the group of people around the table at HHS — physicians and other clinicians, public health professionals, public policy analysts, lawyers, and researchers — all of whom were focused on the challenge of structuring a solution to a complex problem. One result of their work was the Limited English Proficiency Directive (LEPD), issued by the White House in 2000.

The directive covers both healthcare and social services. However, its most revolutionary recommendation stemmed from a landmark United States Supreme Court decision, Lau vs. Nichols, which specified that federal civil rights laws would be satisfied in the case of healthcare only with appropriate interpreter and translation services for people who need them in federally assisted healthcare settings. Because federally funded healthcare settings include tens of thousands of private facilities and managed care organizations that participate in Medicare, Medicaid, SCHIP, and other federal healthcare programs, the effect of the directive was to effectively reach the entire healthcare system. This included physicians in private practice who contract with Medicare, Medicaid, or SCHIP for managed care physician services.

The reception to the directive was, as might be expected, controversial. Characterized as being an "unfunded mandate" — even though the requirements rest on the existence of hundreds of billions of dollars in federal payments — the directive has been met with unhappiness and opposition over the years. At the same time, interpreter and translation services are now a norm at thousands of healthcare institutions and facilities, a testament to the ability of government to slowly impact health practice.

One of the challenges in creating policies to address disparities was the development of the evidence that would justify their existence. At the time, most health insurers had no data on the race, ethnicity, or language preferences of their enrollees or beneficiaries. Lurie and Perez realized that getting anyone to see whether disparities existed was nearly impossible. Initially, health insurers resisted collecting data on race and ethnicity because they thought it was illegal, but Perez carefully researched both federal and state laws and found that collecting such data was legal. From a civil rights point of view, it was problematic that people from different racial or ethnic backgrounds were getting different kinds — and quality — of care. This called for measuring healthcare disparities based on race and ethnicity and language. Simply arriving at the point at which the data could be examined turned out to be an enormous challenge because of the widespread belief among insurers and institutions that the mere act of *collecting* data on healthcare use by national origin would violate civil rights laws.   ●   One of the most important tasks for the HHS Office for Civil Rights, therefore, was to convince insurers and healthcare providers that such data collection was lawful.

> One of the most important tasks for the HHS Office for Civil Rights, therefore, was to convince insurers and healthcare providers that such data collection was lawful.
>
>

Once agency officials began to analyze the data that existed, it became evident that Hispanics, like African-Americans, experienced significant disparities in healthcare. In disentangling the data further, two facts emerged. First was the extent to which having a primary language other than English was a major factor in access and appropriate utilization. The other was the extent to which low health literacy factors, such as educational attainment and health insurance coverage, appeared to be associated with reduced healthcare access.[16]

Health disparities can, in fact, signal a policy matter under civil rights law, as Perez pointed out to Echeveste at the White House symposium. Federal civil rights laws are implicated if the methods used to administer healthcare services have the effect of reducing access for protected racial and ethnic minority groups. The absence of modifications such as translation and interpreters can amount to a violation of civil rights laws. The violation can be corrected through policy changes to ensure compliance with these laws at institutions that receive federal funds, such as hospitals and clinics.

> "The consequences of failing to ensure meaningful access are life and death in a healthcare setting. It was important to lend the most compelling face to the issue."

Perez observes, "The consequences of failing to ensure meaningful access are life and death in a healthcare setting. It was important to lend the most compelling face to the issue." Developing the data on which the LEPD standards rested, and then carefully developing the standards themselves, was painstaking work that required collaboration among analysts, researchers, healthcare specialists, and lawyers. Separate tasks that also required an exhaustive amount of time included outreach to community advocacy groups, healthcare professionals, and other key stakeholders, as well as identification of existing practice models on which the standards could build.

Even though the LEPD standards came in the wake of the Clinton administration's failed national health reform effort, health disparities were in the national spotlight as a result of efforts led by Dr. David Satcher, the Surgeon General and assistant secretary of health. The Public Health Service's signature blueprint for population health, *Healthy People 2010,* was being developed in 1999 and 2000, and Satcher made the reduction of disparities a priority. Because *Healthy People 2010* had as its overarching framework the elimination of population health disparities associated with race, socioeconomic and educational status, geography, sexual orientation, and other factors, a presidential language directive providing major compliance guidance to the healthcare system essentially rested against this disparities background.

Although the LEPD did not have the force and effect of law — its purpose was to set forth guidelines showing healthcare providers how they *might* comply with federal civil rights laws — the underlying message was unmistakable: the administration placed a high priority on equal access and was prepared to issue the guidance as a presidential directive. So powerful was its impact that the Bush administration retained the guidance with only modest modifications.

●   Lurie underscores the importance of the directive in helping to shape the behavior of community institutions and, ultimately, the behavior of the community residents they serve. To Lurie, the language guidance has been a successful strategy for addressing health disparities but is only one strategy for altering the behavior of community institutions. Viewing the strategy in a larger context, she notes, "Community behavior is linked to individual behavior. When communities fail to offer high-quality services or invest in health and public safety, community residents' own choices and behaviors are affected as well. Individual decisions are formed by community norms, and changing the resources available in communities enables individuals to make healthier choices."

Lurie expresses disappointment that the government lost other important opportunities to use its own data, such as that available to Medicare and Medicaid, to create policies that result in community institutional change around disparities. She notes that

●

Lurie underscores the importance of the directive in helping to shape the behavior of community institutions and, ultimately, the behavior of the community residents they serve.

the private sector is actually taking a leading role in attempting to reduce disparities because of the changing demographics of the nation and because of the long-term impact of disparities on productivity, the work force, and positive economic conditions. She observes that corporations such as Marriott rely on thousands of recent immigrants who, in turn, may have language-access challenges. To be good corporate citizens and attractive employers, such companies expect their insurers and healthcare providers to be responsive to the needs of their employees. ● After all, healthy workers are good for business.

● After all, healthy workers are good for business.

Lurie now leads the RAND Corporation's Center for Population Health and Health Disparities, an initiative funded by the National Institutes of Health. There, she focuses on community and national health disparities issues. She also serves on the faculty of the George Washington University School of Medicine. At RAND, Lurie helps support the National Health Plan Disparities Collaborative, a group of 10 large health insurance plans that covers more than half of the population with employer-sponsored insurance. The collaborative helps health plans implement strategies to get information on the race, ethnicity, and language preferences of their enrollees; to use that information to measure the quality of care furnished to patients across all racial and ethnic groups; to investigate potential disparities; and to design interventions.

Perez has held county level elective office in Montgomery County, Md., and became secretary for labor, licensing and regulation in the state in 2007. From 2001 to 2006, he taught at the University of Maryland Law School and joined the faculty of The George Washington University School of Public Health and Health Services, Department of Health Policy, in 2007. The year before, he ran for state attorney general in the Democratic primary, his first foray into statewide politics. As a law professor, he helped his clinical law students file suit in Maryland to contest the removal of 4,000 legal immigrants, all of them pregnant women and children, from the Medicaid roles.

Both Lurie and Perez believe that the LEPD drives home the importance of formal policy in changing the behavior of community institutions to improve access to care, as well as to enhance the decisions that individuals make when they can communicate clearly with their providers. Their work combines civil rights with health policy at the national level to overcome disparities. At the local level, the work of The California Endowment demonstrates how to effect change by working within communities, tapping their leadership potential and ideas in overcoming health disparities and in impacting policymaking. It also demonstrates that data collected at the local level, and shared widely, can leverage local programs into statewide initiatives. ❀

Local Case Study

Robert Ross
and The California Endowment

Robert Ross, MD

$\mathcal{R}$obert Ross, MD, became chief executive officer of The California Endowment in 2001 following a long career as a pediatrician in Camden, N.J., and in northern Philadelphia, two low-income communities. Ross also served as the public health director in Philadelphia and then in California's San Diego County. His role as the head of one of the nation's largest philanthropic organizations has given him great satisfaction, comparable with what he experienced as a clinician and public health officer, and has afforded him the opportunity to work again at the community level to achieve social change.

The California Endowment was created in 1996 when California's not-for-profit Blue Cross of California insurance plan converted to for-profit status. Legal efforts by the state attorney general ensured that the community assets that had been invested in Blue Cross be returned to the community. The California Endowment is the result of that reinvestment, and its enormous size — $3 billion at the time of the conversion — is a testament to more than 40 years of community investment in Blue Cross.

The mission of The California Endowment is to address health-care access for California's low-income and medically underserved residents at high risk for health disparities. An 18-member board of directors, who are selected because of their community involvement and leadership, oversees The Endowment and its investments. The founding set of principles created by the original board frames everything The Endowment does. Regardless of political popularity, The Endowment remains focused on using its resources to help undocumented children, farm workers, ex-prisoners, and the most vulnerable populations in California gain access to health insurance. Ross says, "We don't see communities as direct objects, as people who need our services. In these communities, leaders have vision, creativity, passion, and the know-how to solve problems.   ●   Our orientation is very much in viewing underserved communities as incubators for solving problems." In addition to community involvement, The Endowment emphasizes prevention and diversity.

During The Endowment's first five years, which preceded Ross' arrival, the board of directors made a series of basic resource-allocation decisions. The board concluded that helping the state's struggling safety net hospitals and clinics meet the cost of uncompensated care would quickly swallow up available resources. As discretionary funds to undertake community and public health innovations are rare, The Endowment's leadership concluded that its funding should move beyond charity and become about change.

In fact, community change is the hallmark of The Endowment's giving. Each year, The Endowment awards approximately $160 million in grants, less than half of one percent of California's total annual spending on Medicaid. At the same time, Ross notes, "The fundamental question for a philanthropy with a focus on public health is that simply adding charitable funds to existing programs results little in the way of real change." Instead, The Endowment chose to move in the direction of policy and system change rather than a more simple charity route.

Examples abound of The Endowment's funded programs, many of which are making change possible. In 2000, a grassroots community coalition in Santa Clara County proposed that every child in the county, regardless of documentation status, be guaranteed health insurance coverage. The Endowment perceived the proposal as being about change and helped fund the effort in collaboration with other private foundations. Indeed, so many counties in the state followed Santa Clara County's lead that in

●

"Our orientation is very much in viewing underserved communities as incubators for solving problems."

2006, the California Legislature enacted universal health insurance coverage for children. Budget constraints and controversy over coverage for undocumented children led to a gubernatorial veto, but the notion of statewide universal coverage for children lives on throughout the state. Of California's 63 counties, 18 have made all children eligible for health insurance coverage. In partnership with other funders, The Endowment leveraged its modest support of the Santa Clara County proposal to create a statewide movement.

Another example of The Endowment's community initiatives with statewide policy payoffs has been Healthy Eating, Active Communities. This initiative has won the support of Gov. Arnold Schwarzenegger and first lady Maria Shriver because of its potential to affect the childhood obesity epidemic, which hits minority populations and low-income communities with particular ferocity. ● Without change, one in three children born to African-American and Hispanic families in 2007 will develop diabetes, a statistic that compelled The Endowment to act.

●

Without change, one in three children born to African-American and Hispanic families in 2007 will develop diabetes, a statistic that compelled The Endowment to act.

To encourage healthy eating and physical activity, The Endowment helps underwrite efforts to introduce fresh fruits and vegetables and safe play areas into communities. A grassroots coalition of citizen activists, known as Healthy Eating, Active Communities, received a $26 million multiyear grant from The Endowment to leverage initiatives in an ever-growing number of communities. The coalition prompted Schwarzenegger, a strong advocate of physical fitness, to convene a health summit aimed at seeking ways to alter the childhood obesity problem. McDonald's, the Coca-Cola Company, PepsiCo, and Safeway were all invited to the summit, and Schwarzenegger signed into law a bill, long-stalled, that eliminated junk food and soda from public schools.

LC Prime and Second Chance, two other programs that The Endowment supports, are also models for change. LC Prime began at the University of California-Irvine School of Medicine, which sets aside eight places each year for Hispanic medical students to participate in a special five-year program to build medical care capacity in underserved communities. The program's key feature, a half-year immersion program in Mexico so that students can experience Mexican culture firsthand, has been so successful at building cultural competency that other state-supported medical schools in California plan to adopt the program. A substantial $600,000 grant from The Endowment helped start LC Prime. Over time and as each graduate returns to the community, the imbalance of practicing Hispanic physicians in California will diminish.

Second Chance began in San Diego as a job training program for ex-felons with the aim of reversing a 70 percent recidivism rate. Drugs, alcohol, and depression are often the root causes for ex-felons returning to prison. Second Chance focuses on offering treatment as soon as prisoners are released. The Endowment provided seed money and underwrote program evaluation, as it does with all of its programs. The two-year evaluation of Second Chance demonstrated a remarkable turnaround for ex-felons who participated in the program; more than 70 percent were keeping jobs and paying taxes. Such success encouraged communities across the state to adopt the Second Chance approach. The Endowment, once again, leveraged a program for change.

●   In this case, it helped state policymakers reduce prison re-entry, with an annual savings of $35,000 per inmate.

●

In this case, it helped state policymakers reduce prison re-entry, with an annual savings of $35,000 per inmate.

Ross says, "We learned in the children's health coverage approach that if you want to move a policy agenda, you've got to have concrete examples of change going on locally and it's got to be connected to a broader policy strategy." He adds, "Being a good listener and learning from our grantees has been very fruitful for us." The paradigm shift at The California Endowment goes outside the four walls of the healthcare system and attempts to rethink health beyond doctors, patients, clinics, and hospitals. The Endowment focuses on neighborhoods, poverty, and racism in an effort to broaden the discussion about health to matters that lie beyond the limits of healthcare.

Perhaps the most remarkable aspect of The Endowment is that in its affirmative and long-term commitment to community health, as well as its sustained investment in people and reforms in policy and practice, The Endowment is becoming a national model for what a health foundation can achieve. Nationally, private health foundations are focusing more intently on supporting policy and advocacy in healthcare. The Endowment's ability to make a difference even in a highly challenging political climate shows the important impact that comes from investing in policy innovation from the ground up. ❈

Lessons Learned

*R*educing disparities in health and healthcare lies at the heart of both case studies. The approaches taken by Lurie, Perez, Ross, and The California Endowment are very different, yet they all share the common goal of leveling the healthcare playing field for all members of society. Following are the lessons learned from their case studies.

The Role of Public Health in Policy

Overcoming health disparities has been a major focus of the public health community in the last decade. Because of the many factors that lead to health disparities, a "one size fits all" approach to solving the issue will not work. ● The work of Lurie and Perez demonstrates that by chipping away at one area of the problem — language barriers — other health and healthcare problems are positively impacted as well.

Ross' work with The California Endowment focuses on supporting programs and models that create positive change, rather than on continuing to fund existing systems that do not address larger disparities issues. Even a decision viewed as purely revenue driven, such as the conversion by Blue Cross of California to for-profit status, can have a positive impact on population health. Leveraging the funds from the conversion to create The California Endowment led to the development of an organization committed to addressing the unmet healthcare needs of under-served populations through policy change and community mobilization.

Sound Policy Analysis in Public Health Practice

All healthcare policy is local, even when it is implemented at the national level. Lurie, Perez, and Ross would agree that national policy depends on local data because the delivery of care and prevention are happening at the individual and community level.

●
The work of Lurie and Perez demonstrates that by chipping away at one area of the problem — language barriers — other health and healthcare problems are positively impacted as well.

Lurie's and Perez's case study shows that, however mundane it may seem, data at the local level on race, ethnicity, and language preference are essential for addressing disparities and creating sound health policy and practice.

The California Endowment, under Ross' leadership, has been willing to invest in innovative concepts and communities that bring multidisciplinary skills to public health problems. Simple charity giving would help institutions but might not change communities. The Endowment emphasizes prevention and diversity and views underserved communities as being the incubators for solving a community's health problems.

The Role of Individuals

The story of the Limited English Proficiency Directive shows the enormous results that can be achieved when individuals with multiple policy skills come together to solve a problem. Lurie is a physician and a public health researcher. Perez is a civil rights lawyer. Together, they demonstrated a profound ability to recognize a policy window of opportunity, amassed the evidence essential to documenting the importance of a policy intervention, and drafted and shaped the policy. Neither could have achieved this outcome alone. The results depended on a combination of policy skills spanning law and health services research, as well as on a deep and abiding public health orientation toward social change in institutions that, in turn, would affect the health of individuals.

Ross emphasizes that being a good listener and learning from grantees have been very fruitful for The Endowment.

●
Individuals who have a core set of values and a clear vision are those who can best define policy.

● Individuals who have a core set of values and a clear vision are those who can best define policy. Ross, following the example set by The Endowment's original board, decided to move beyond charity and into health policy and system change. By leveraging its resources for the health system and for community mobilization, the Endowment has had a broad and positive impact on the health status of underserved populations in California.

Advocacy for Public Health Policy

To implement policy change in healthcare delivery for diverse
populations, policymakers must work with communities,
advocacy groups, and healthcare professionals. Together, they can
identify good practices and policy solutions that will overcome
these healthcare barriers. Both case studies strongly focus on the
recognition that neighborhoods, poverty, and racism all impact
the delivery of healthcare in a community. ● The best
solutions involve whole communities and rethink the healthcare
system beyond doctors, patients, clinics, and hospitals.

Whether it is providing an interpreter for a patient who must
make a medical decision or helping an ex-felon cope with life
outside prison, Lurie, Perez, and Ross share a common aspiration:
that public health will learn how to achieve fundamental social
reforms through broad vision and the enlistment of community
leaders from across all sectors. ❀ ❀

●

The best
solutions
involve whole
communities
and rethink the
healthcare system
beyond doctors,
patients, clinics,
and hospitals.

References

1. Goldberg J, Hayes, W, Huntley J; Health Policy Institute of Ohio. Understanding health disparities. Nov. 2004. [cited 2007 Aug 23]. Available from: http://www.healthpolicyohio.org/pdf/healthdisparities.pdf.

2. American Public Health Association (APHA). Eliminating health disparities: toolkit (2004.) [cited 2007 Aug 23]. Available from: http://www.apha.org/NPHW/toolkit/Toolkit-PHW04-LR.pdf.

3. American Public Health Association (APHA). Eliminating health disparities: Communities moving from statistics to solutions—Toolkit. Washington, DC: American Public Health Association, 2004.

4. National Center for Health Statistics. Health, United States, 2002, Table 30. Cited in: Office of Minority Health and Health Disparities, Centers for Disease Control and Prevention [Home page on the Internet]. Atlanta: Disease burden and risk factors. [updated 2007 Jun 5; cited 2007 Aug 23]. Available from: http://www.cdc.gov/omhd/AMH/dbrf.htm.

5. National Center for Health Statistics. Health, United States, 2002, Table 30. Cited in: Office of Minority Health and Health Disparities, Centers for Disease Control and Prevention [Home page on the Internet]. Atlanta: Disease burden and risk factors. [updated 2007 Jun 5; cited 2007 Aug 23]. Available from: http://www.cdc.gov/omhd/AMH/dbrf.htm.

6. National Center for Chronic Disease Prevention and Health Promotion, Centers for Disease Control [Home page on the Internet]. Atlanta: National diabetes fact sheet. 2000. [updated 2005 Jan 31; cited 2007 Sept 18]. Available from: http://www.cdc.gov/diabetes/pubs/estimates.htm.

7. National Center for Health Statistics. Health, United States, 2002, Table 54. Cited in: Office of Minority Health and Health Disparities, Centers for Disease Control and Prevention [Home page on the Internet]. Atlanta: Disease burden and risk factors. [updated 2007 Jun 5; cited 2007 Aug 23]. Available from: http://www.cdc.gov/omhd/AMH/dbrf.htm.

8. National Center for Health Statistics. Health, United States, 2002, Table 54. Cited in: Office of Minority Health and Health Disparities, Centers for Disease Control and Prevention [Home page on the Internet]. Atlanta: Disease burden and risk factors. [updated 2007 Jun 5; cited 2007 Aug 23]. Available from: http://www.cdc.gov/omhd/AMH/dbrf.htm.

9. Centers for Disease Control. Morbidity and mortality weekly report. 2002 Nov 15; 51(45): 1020. Available from: http://www.cdc.gov/mmwr/PDF/wk/mm5145.pdf.

10. Laditka JN, Laditka SB. Race, ethnicity and hospitalization for six chronic ambulatory care sensitive conditions in the USA. *Ethnicity and Health*. 2006 Aug; 11(3). 247-263.

11. Goldberg J, Hayes, W, Huntley J; Health Policy Institute of Ohio. Understanding health disparities. November 2004. [cited 2007 Aug 23]. Available from: http://www.healthpolicyohio.org/pdf/healthdisparities.pdf.

12. Goldberg J, Hayes, W, Huntley J; Health Policy Institute of Ohio. Understanding health disparities. November 2004. [cited 2007 Aug 23]. Available from: http://www.healthpolicyohio.org/pdf/healthdisparities.pdf

13. Goldberg J, Hayes, W, Huntley J; Health Policy Institute of Ohio. Understanding health disparities. November 2004. [cited 2007 Aug 23]. Available from: http://www.healthpolicyohio.org/pdf/healthdisparities.pdf.

14. Chin MH, Chien AT. Reducing racial and ethnic disparities in health care: an integral part of quality improvement scholarship. *Quality and Safety in Health Care*. 2006; 15: 79-80.

15. Agency for Healthcare Research and Quality [Home page on the Internet]. Rockville: Addressing health care disparities: promising approaches. Presentation given by LaVerne Wiley and Carolyn Jenkins. [cited 2007 Aug 23]. Available from: http://www.ahrq.gov/news/ulp/addispar/addisp4.htm.

16. Schillinger D, Grumbach K, Piette J, Wang F, Osmond D, Daher C, Palacios J, Diaz Sullivan G, Bindman AB. Association of health literacy with diabetes outcomes. *Journal of the American Medical Association*. 2002; 288(4):475-482.

Chapter 4. **Changing the Landscape:**
           Embedding Quality and Patient
           Safety Into Healthcare Delivery

Introduction

$\mathcal{T}$he saying goes, "To err is human. To forgive, divine."
Unfortunately this is not the case when it comes to medical
care. Errors in medical care — no matter how unintentional —
can have fatal consequences. Ensuring the quality and safety of
healthcare in the United States has become a major focus of
public health research and practice since the Institute of Medicine
(IOM) released its influential report, *The Future of Public Health*,
in the 1990s.[1]   ●   Research demonstrates that the country's
healthcare delivery system does not provide consistent, high
quality care to all people.[2] In response to this, a movement
has developed over the last decade that links public health and
medicine. This movement has led to policies that now require
that healthcare quality and safety be measured and tracked.
Measurement leads to interventions and policies that seek
to improve the delivery of high quality care which, in turn,
measures progress and drives toward even wider delivery of
optimal care. Patient safety has become the catchphrase of
this public health movement.

●

Research
demonstrates
that the country's
healthcare
delivery system
does not provide
consistent,
high quality care
to all people.

Public health experts point to three main factors that make
patient safety and quality of care dominant issues in public
health. First, medical science and technology have advanced at
an unprecedented rate during the past half century. However, the
nation's healthcare delivery system has fallen short in translating
knowledge into practice and applying new technology safely and
appropriately. Second, the healthcare needs of the population
have changed. Chronic diseases are now the leading cause of
illness, disability, and death, and the current health system is not
well-suited to treating them appropriately and efficaciously.

People with chronic conditions need multidisciplinary services and infrastructure, and there simply aren't enough programs that meet these criteria. Third, the healthcare delivery system is poorly organized. Delivery of care is overly complex and uncoordinated, and the sequenced steps and patient handoffs required often slow down care, leading to a decrease rather than an improvement in safety.[3]

Patient safety and quality healthcare have related goals. To improve patient safety, for example, medical errors need to be prevented. If errors do occur, lessons must be learned in order to prevent them in the future. ● For lessons to be learned quickly, the healthcare industry should streamline the way in which professionals acquire, share, and act on information related to error prevention and quality improvement.[4] Surveillance lies at the heart of acquiring this information. The Centers for Disease Control and Prevention (CDC) defines surveillance as the ongoing systematic collection, analysis, and interpretation of health-related data essential to planning, implementing, and evaluating the practice of public health. Once collected, surveillance data needs to reach those responsible for disease prevention and control in a timely manner so that interventions can be applied.[5] This same approach can be applied to the measuring and monitoring of healthcare delivery.

●

For lessons to be learned quickly, the healthcare industry should streamline the way in which professionals acquire, share, and act on information related to error prevention and quality improvement.

Surveillance data can also be used to detect and identify low quality performance in healthcare. In interpreting surveillance data, health agencies at all levels need to be aware of current clinical guidelines, standards of care, accepted community practices, long-term trends, and patterns of performance among providers to the populations they serve. A good surveillance system detects deviations from those standards and notices any changes in practice patterns. By monitoring existing patterns, agencies can forecast patterns and set priorities that assist in planning, implementing, and evaluating medical and public health interventions and solutions.[6]

In the early to mid-1990s, Lucian Leape, MD, culminated years of research by publishing several important papers on the epidemiology of medical errors. These papers set the stage for current work in the field. In 1994, his groundbreaking article, *Error in Medicine*, introduced the concept that systems, rather than individuals, cause medical errors.[7] In June 1998, responding to the need for change, IOM created the Committee on the Quality of Health Care in America and charged it with developing a strategy to substantially improve the quality of healthcare over the next 10 years.[8] During that same year, Vice President Al Gore released a U.S. Department of Health and Human Services (HHS) report, *The Challenges and Potential for Assuring Quality Health Care for 21st Century*, which proposed a coordinated national approach to quality measuring and reporting that would address wide-ranging quality problems in the healthcare industry.[9]

In 2000, the IOM published a sentinel report on medical errors, *To Err Is Human: Building a Safer Health System*, to which Leape was a key contributor. ● The report cited preventable death as a leading cause of death and estimated that between 44,000 and 98,000 Americans die each year in hospitals as a result of medical errors. The report gained widespread media attention for recommending major changes to the healthcare system.[10]

●

The report cited preventable death as a leading cause of death and estimated that between 44,000 and 98,000 Americans die each year in hospitals as a result of medical errors.

Since the release of *To Err Is Human*, a number of national and private initiatives have tried to define the scope of the problem and develop strategies for quality improvement. The Agency for Healthcare Research and Quality (AHRQ) and the National Quality Forum are the leading agencies coordinating research activity and implementing standards for quality improvement. In addition, the Joint Commission has called for implementing new patient safety standards and mandatory nonpunitive reporting of serious medical errors.[11]

Likewise, the CDC is working with leading employers and the National Business Coalition on Health to refine the instrument for the common Request for Information, currently used to solicit information from more than 85 major health plans. The National Committee for Quality Assurance developed measures for the Health Plan Employer Data and Information Set, creating 50 measures designed to help employers and other healthcare purchasers evaluate the performance of the majority of the nation's health plans.

In addition, the American Medical Association (AMA) and several private corporations founded the National Patient Safety Foundation (NPSF) in 1996 as an independent, nonprofit research and education organization committed to making patient safety a national priority.[12] ● Because of the efforts of NPSF and other organizations, patient safety reporting systems have mushroomed in recent years.[13] Many hospitals now routinely capture information on medical errors, although these reporting systems still have limitations. Often, the collected data are neither complete nor standardized, and reporting can be costly, cumbersome, and sporadic. It is still difficult to quantify the full magnitude of quality and safety challenges with certainty. Achieving a new standard in healthcare requires that all stake-holders be committed to a culture of safety and improved information systems.[14]

●

Because of the efforts of NPSF and other organizations, patient safety reporting systems have mushroomed in recent years.

Influencing patient safety policies is delicate work. Experts in the field hope to ensure the participation of healthcare providers and institutions by creating a culture of safety, rather than one of policing and punishment. Leadership in this arena must be exercised in a strategic and thought-provoking manner and must provide decision makers with examples of evidence-based medicine and best practices.

Leape has been at the forefront of this issue. He was instrumental in calling attention to the need for monitoring the quality of care and has made patient safety a leading issue in the debate about healthcare reform. His work in making patient safety a national priority is a case study in going against the grain of an established system to create something better. Furthering this cause, the work of Edward Hannan, PhD, shows how patient safety can be measured and impacted through the careful monitoring and reporting of care at the local level. Dr. Hannan helped establish a coronary artery bypass graft (CABG) surgery reporting system at the New York State Department of Health. This monitoring system tracks surgery outcomes at hospitals across the state, instilling a focus on quality in surgical procedures. Feeding this information back to practitioners has allowed them to improve their practices and patient care. Statistics prove that New York's approach saves lives, but to date, only a handful of other states have followed suit. ✺

National Case Study

Lucian Leape and *To Err Is Human*

*E*very successful movement has a champion, one who is willing to raise his or her voice despite the objections of colleagues or an established system. Patient safety's earliest champion may be Lucian Leape, MD. A pediatric surgeon, Leape became engaged in issues of quality of care and patient safety by happenstance. While on sabbatical from Harvard Medical School at the RAND Corporation in Santa Monica, California, he knew he wanted to transition into the policy arena after 25 years as a surgeon, and he zeroed in on the issues that have consumed him ever since.

Lucian Leape, MD

When Leape returned to Harvard, Howard Hiatt, MD, former dean of the School of Public Health, encouraged him to expand his policy focus by participating in the Medical Practice Study. That study, performed in the late 1980s with 30,000 hospital patients in New York, found that 3.7 percent of patients admitted into acute care hospitals had an injury from medical treatment and that 13.6 percent died as a result. When he reviewed the data in 1989, Leape was struck by the fact that more than two-thirds of the injuries and deaths were caused by physician or provider errors.

Leape spent countless hours at the Countway Library at the Harvard School of Public Health, reviewing the literature on preventing medical errors, only to find a limited number of articles or studies on the issue. He turned instead to the humanities literature, steeping himself over the next year in articles about human factor engineering and cognitive psychology. People had been studying human error for 50 years, just not in the medical field. He discovered James Reason's definitive work on human error and told himself, "If I don't know it, other people don't know it either." While human error had been addressed in aviation, chemical manufacturing, and other hazardous industries, remedies for preventing medical error were almost nonexistent. In fact, knowledge of the entire field was largely unknown in healthcare.

Leape had seen six Navy pilots killed on his aircraft carrier during his military service, so preventing error resonated with him. He published his first paper on the subject, *Error in Medicine*, at the end of 1994. ● In it, he made the case that healthcare could apply the lessons from human factor engineering to reduce medical errors and injuries. *The New England Journal of Medicine* rejected the article, but George Lundberg, then editor of the *Journal of the American Medical Association (JAMA)*, published it, despite heavy objections from colleagues and stakeholders. Leape is pleased that Lundberg recently confided to him that this paper was the most important he had ever published.

●

In it, he made the case that healthcare could apply the lessons from human factor engineering to reduce medical errors and injuries.

Error in Medicine received little notice when first published, but it gained a toehold for a movement that Leape was willing to spearhead. He began to think about the kind of research that would prove the validity of the concept that medical error could be prevented by changing systems, and he has been focusing on this policy challenge ever since. As all doctors, even surgeons, write prescriptions, the medication system was a logical starting point for identifying systems failures that lead to errors. Medication errors affect everyone across the healthcare spectrum, including all clinical specialties, nursing, and pharmacy, but an entrenched system was in place. The first phase of Leape's work, studying that system, helped him understand why failures occur.

With his colleague, David Bates, MD, Leape carried out a study at two major teaching hospitals affiliated with the Harvard Medical School (Massachusetts General and Brigham and Women's) that measured the extent of medication errors. The study, published in *JAMA* in 1995, identified multiple systems failures. Two years later, Leape and Bates introduced two major system changes at these hospitals: computerized order entry at Brigham and Women's, and pharmacists accompanying clinicians on morning rounds at Massachusetts General. Brigham and Women's had already begun to convert to computerized order entry from paper prescriptions, and the study hastened that conversion. At Massachusetts General, which was not yet ready for computerized order entry, Leape and Bates hypothesized that a pharmacist participating in morning rounds might reduce physicians' prescribing errors. At both hospitals, the system changes proved to be highly effective in reducing errors. Brigham and Women's proceeded with implementing computerized order entry, and Massachusetts General implemented pharmacist shadowing in all of its intensive care units.

Leape says, ● "It's a fundamental conceptual change, a major paradigm shift, for doctors and nurses to think about systems instead of individual performance. It has proved to be powerful, and yet we've only scratched the surface; we've just barely begun." Systems issues include not only confusing labels and packaging of drugs and poorly written prescriptions but also factors that affect individual performance, such as physicians in training who have been kept up all night and who have been trained inadequately and supervised poorly.

> ●
> "It's a fundamental conceptual change, a major paradigm shift, for doctors and nurses to think about systems instead of individual performance."

Moving into a new policy phase, Leape participated in the writing of the in-depth IOM report, *To Err Is Human*, which reviewed all the work in the field and brought theories together. The report was published in late 1999 and received widespread media attention and immediate acclaim from the public and policymakers. The issue of patient safety had finally made its mark on a wider stage.

Leape says, "The ultimate threat to patient safety now is our failure to do what we know how to do — to implement known safe practices. It's not quite the same thing as making an error, but it's a systems issue clearly. The systems don't work. All of the big public health problems are essentially systems and safety issues in the sense of not providing good care." He points out that injury from treatment is the fourth leading cause of death in the U.S., as much a public health problem as cancer or heart disease. He adds, "The cornerstone of safety is prevention of injury.

● The concept that our major challenge is to prevent injuries, not merely take care of them, is very much in the classic public health model."

> ● "The concept that our major challenge is to prevent injuries, not merely take care of them, is very much in the classic public health model."

Leape's studies, combined with the IOM report, galvanized the public health and policy worlds. At the national level, AHRQ has led the way toward improving quality of care and patient safety. AHRQ supports the National Quality Forum (NQF), a nongovernmental, multi-stakeholder organization that has become a major force for national policy. Leape co-chaired the forum's first effort at standard-setting in the area of serious adverse events reporting. The next NQF effort, perhaps even more important at the clinical practice level, was defining safe practices. The forum recommended 30 evidence-based safe practices, some as complicated as computer order entry and others as simple as disinfection protocols and procedures to ensure against wrong-side surgery.

The other major national player in the field, the Joint Commission, seized on patient safety issues in 1996 by launching a nonpunitive adverse events reporting program. The ability to report errors without fear of punishment or legal action is extremely important to the success of the patient safety movement. Until the healthcare community feels that they can discuss their errors, with the intention of learning from and correcting procedures, it will be hard for full-scale prevention to be achieved.

At the hospital level, establishing nonpunitive environments for discussing medical errors has been an important policy step, as has been implementing safe practices. More than 3,100 hospitals across the country participate in the Institute for Healthcare Improvement's (IHI) "Protecting 5 Million Lives From Harm" campaign (originally the "100,000 Lives" campaign), agreeing to maintain an ongoing focus on patient safety and system changes.

From 1995 to 2000, the Veterans Health Administration under Ken Kizer's leadership put safety on the front burner through the VA Patient Safety Program. This nonpunitive accountability system deals with adverse events as they arise and sees each event through to a resolution by involving the entire chain of command. In 1999, the VA established the National Center for Patient Safety, led by former astronaut James Bagian, MD, which has proved to be an important and ongoing effort to develop and nurture a culture of safety throughout the VA system.

Leape welcomes the many positive changes he sees in hospital-based patient safety. Nearly all hospitals have made systems changes in responding to the challenge, but he observes that safety is still not a top priority for most healthcare organizations. He notes that in the U.S. healthcare financing environment, there is no penalty for bad care; in fact, there is a bonus because treating complications earns more money. Leape says, ● "We have a financing system for healthcare in America that works against quality and safety in that it rewards poor care and often penalizes good care." Incentives for healthcare leaders to change this dynamic are currently not great enough, and physicians themselves often think of patient safety as someone else's problem. Accountability is a crucial aspect of patient safety, and physicians still need to be brought on board in order for prevention of injury to become a successful cornerstone in public health.

> ●
> "We have a financing system for healthcare in America that works against quality and safety in that it rewards poor care and often penalizes good care."

Leape works at the highly visible national level to improve patient safety and remains, by choice, outside formal government structures. He says that federal government efforts are inadequate thus far and believes that there is something fundamentally wrong when the funding for finding a cure for malaria comes from a private foundation rather than from concerted governmental activity. Leape's efforts to shed light on these issues at the national level has fortunately led to actual accomplishments at local levels of care.

A case in point is the coronary artery bypass graft (CABG) surgery reporting system established by the New York State Department of Health. This story examines the work of Edward Hannan, whose surveillance and cardiac data-monitoring system helped to change cardiac surgery outcomes by improving the quality of surgical care delivered in hospitals in New York. ❁

Local Case Study

Edward Hannan
and New York's CABG Surgery Reporting System

*T*he educational background of Edward Hannan, PhD, affords him a unique perspective on public health and helped pave the way to astounding improvements in hospital-based quality of care and patient safety. Currently a distinguished professor and associate dean for research at the University at Albany School of Public Health, Hannan earned his doctorate in operations research at the University of Massachusetts, rare academic training for a public health professional. The project that Hannan spearheaded at the New York State Department of Health (NYSDOH), and in which he is still involved at the University at Albany, was a coronary artery bypass graft (CABG) surgery reporting system that developed risk-adjusted mortality rates for all CABG surgeries at hospitals throughout New York. Perhaps most importantly, the system made these data public in an annual report so that the public, payers, and policymakers could evaluate outcomes from different hospitals.

Edward Hannan, PhD

Hannan worked at NYSDOH from 1980 until 1990 as director of the Bureau of Health Care Research and Information Services. In that capacity, he played a central role in creating the cardiac surgery reporting system, along with a long-standing Cardiac Advisory Committee (CAC) made up of surgeons, cardiologists, health policy experts, and consumer advocates. For years, the CAC had overseen hospital performance in bypass and valve surgery by using only information about the number of patients and the overall mortality rate for each procedure in each hospital. Huge variations occurred, but there was no way to determine the extent to which they were related to quality of care or to differences in the severity of the patient's illness before the surgery. When the committee approached a hospital with an unusually high mortality rate, the usual defense was that patients at their hospital were sicker than everyone else's. There was no way to confirm whether this was true.

In late 1988, Hannan helped develop a new patient-specific database, where hospitals performing CABG surgeries were required to account for how sick each patient was, as well as their risk factors, based on information in the published literature about adverse outcomes in bypass surgery. How old were the patients? Had they suffered a previous heart attack?

●   Accumulating the data on these individuals would allow for an overall demographic profile of each hospital. Analyzing data from the forms would allow the NYSDOH to find a mathematical way to even the playing field by adjusting outcomes according to differences in the severity of patient illness, which would, in turn, encourage hospitals to keep accepting the sickest patients. NYSDOH already had a useful acute-care patient reporting system called SPARCS (for Statewide Planning and Research Cooperative System) long in place for hospital reimbursement. SPARCS could now be used to check a hospital's submitted CABG data to ensure that all cases were accounted for. However, SPARCS alone did not contain the necessary detail for risk-adjusting outcomes.

At the time the system was created, 29 hospitals (of 250 in the state) were performing the CABG procedure and roughly 15,000 patients per year underwent isolated CABG surgery in New York. To be truly useful to hospitals and the public as a valid measure of quality of care, CABG data had to be adjusted to reflect the health status of patients who received the procedure. Patients with advanced coronary disease, older patients, and patients with multiple co-morbidities posed a far greater risk of death than their younger or healthier counterparts.

Making this data public was very controversial in the healthcare community. Hospitals and surgeons felt as if they were under

●
Accumulating the data on these individuals would allow for an overall demographic profile for each hospital.

attack for taking risks to try to save lives, and they resented the possible sting of public outcry. Nonetheless, the New York State commissioner of health at that time, Dr. David Axelrod, believed that releasing the CABG surgery data was an important tool for achieving his department's primary responsibility — ensuring the safety of New Yorkers.   ●   He felt that without the glare of publicity, incentives to improve systems in hospitals would lack bite. Fortunately, the NYSDOH had the power needed to make this happen. The department's Certificate of Need system determines which hospitals can provide advanced surgical procedures to treat coronary artery disease, and this gave Axelrod leverage in enforcing the new measurement. For his part, the commissioner never shirked from regulations that could improve patient safety.

> ●
>
> [Axelrod] felt that without the glare of publicity, incentives to improve systems in hospitals would lack bite.

In 1989, the first annual CABG surgery tracking report was published, but just for internal distribution to the hospitals. In 1990, Hannan and his colleagues published a manuscript in *JAMA* that detailed the methods used to risk-adjust the outcomes; they provided specific risk-adjusted outcomes with the hospital names encrypted.[38] Shortly afterward, Axelrod released the hospitals' unencrypted risk-adjusted mortality rates to *The New York Times*, causing an intense furor about lost confidentiality. Then another newspaper, *Newsday*, filed a lawsuit against NYSDOH seeking surgeon-level data, which they won in court. For the first time, the public could now see the outcomes for individual surgeons performing CABG and could make decisions based on the data. Despite objections from the medical community, similar data for angioplasties were released in 1992.

An important part of the data system is the validity of the data, especially when it is made public. Hannan recalls when a hospital submitted more than 400 cases to the Health Department with no deaths. Thanks to the SPARCS system, a cross-check revealed that the hospital had omitted 32 patient cases, 18 of whom had died. The hospital's mortality rate suddenly rose from virtually zero to nearly five percent. The CABG data submitted by hospitals must be constantly audited, a task that the Department of Health continues to perform in order to ensure quality and validity.

What are the advantages of making public these previously sacrosanct data? New York's history offers guidance. The primary purpose of the data was to feed information back to hospitals, surgeons, and cardiologists to help them improve their performance. Without data being made public, hospitals could question the validity of the report and would not need to examine their processes of care related to adverse outcomes. However, in the public's eye, hospitals wanted to prove that they were taking measures to improve quality and patient safety.   ● In one sense, making the data public became a self-fulfilling way to sharpen the hospitals' focus on improving quality.

● In one sense, making the data public became a self-fulfilling way to sharpen the hospitals' focus on improving quality.

Over the years in New York, only a few hospitals have suspended performing CABG surgeries based on risk-adjusted mortality rates, usually on a voluntary basis and for brief periods of time. In fact, the number of hospitals performing the procedure has grown, none have dropped off the list, and most have achieved improvements in overall mortality rates. Specifically, the in-hospital mortality rate for isolated CABG surgery in New York decreased 55 percent, from 3.52 percent in 1989[15] to 1.60 percent in 2004.[16] This substantial decrease occurred despite the fact that, according to Hannan, the average CABG surgery patient was sicker before surgery in 2004 than in 1989.

Recent technical improvements in the way that the procedure is performed has led to a different and more accurate measure of the value of the New York program — comparison of mortality rates and mortality rate changes in New York relative to other states. A 1998 study in the *Journal of the American College of Cardiology* found that between 1987 and 1992, unadjusted 30-day mortality rates following bypass declined by 33 percent in New York Medicare patients, compared with a 19 percent decline nationwide. As a result of this improvement, New York had the lowest risk-adjusted bypass mortality rate of any state in 1992.[17]

Another study by Hannan and his colleagues in 2004 demonstrated that between 1994 and 1999, Medicare CABG surgery patients in states other than New York were roughly one and a half times more likely to die in the hospital during the same hospital stay as their surgery, or within 30 days of surgery, as were New York Medicare CABG surgery patients. As always, the results were adjusted for preoperative severity of illness.[18]

New York was the first state to make public any procedural or medical outcomes data. Pennsylvania quickly followed suit with CABG data in 1991. Today, California, Florida, Massachusetts, and New Jersey also release their CABG data. However, New York continues to be a leader in reporting and making public the data for valve surgery, pediatric cardiac surgery, and angioplasty. European countries, including the United Kingdom and Italy, have initiated efforts to release their CABG surgery data, and efforts are also under way to follow suit in Australia. Notably, the highly publicized Pay for Performance Initiative of the Center for Medicare and Medicaid Services, which has resulted in the recent release of hospital outcomes for heart attack and congestive heart failure patients, is an extension of the effort started in New York 18 years ago.[19]   ●   What started as a statewide effort has now blossomed into a national and international effort to supply the public with its right-to-know information on quality of care, as well as to spur providers to improve the quality of care they deliver to patients.

Furthermore, the data systems have helped expand published literature on quality of care and patient safety. Hannan and others have used the New York CABG surgery, valve, pediatric cardiac surgery, and angioplasty databases in more than 50 peer-reviewed studies, which have been published in journals such as *The New England Journal of Medicine, Journal of the American Medical Association, Circulation, Journal of the American College of Cardiology,* and numerous other medical and health services research journals. Among the examined issues are assessments of the impact of public release

●

What started as a statewide effort has now blossomed into a national and international effort to supply the public with its right-to-know information on quality of care.

of data,[20-25] development of risk indexes to be used for determination of treatment and informed consent for patients,[26-28] the impact of provider volume on surgery and angioplasty outcomes,[29-36] access to appropriate cardiac care, documentation of health disparities in access to care,[37-38] and comparisons of competing treatments (for example, CABG surgery versus angioplasty).[39-45] ✻

Lessons Learned

*L*eape and Hannan provide two models of leadership. Leape has attained national visibility as a policy provocateur, and Hannan works in the policy trenches, promoting evidenced-based medicine as a means to improve healthcare quality and patient safety. Both approaches reveal important lessons for future leaders.

The Role of Public Health in Policy

As a pediatric surgeon for 25 years, Leape sought to move beyond saving lives one by one to see how he might influence policy in a way that could save countless lives all at once. Through much research, he discovered that patient safety is a systems issue.

● Prevention of injury in hospitals, as much as cancer and heart disease, deserves the full attention of the healthcare and public health communities.

The U.S. healthcare system currently rewards acute care instead of preventive care, and has minimal penalties for poor care. Leape and Hannan have sought to change this paradigm. For hospital-based patient safety to continue to make inroads, systems must be changed to reward quality and safety. Patient safety can be achieved through health policy as well as through innovative monitoring and implementation programs.

●

Prevention of injury in hospitals, as much as cancer and heart disease, deserves the full attention of the healthcare and public health communities.

Sound Policy Analysis in Public Health Practice

The annual New York CABG surgery reporting system is an example of how a surveillance and monitoring system built on public health principles can be a route to improving performance and, thus, improved healthcare quality and patient safety.

Hannan knew that collecting and analyzing risk-adjusted hospital and practice data in a transparent manner is critical to maintaining the public's trust. Such data can be used to impact the application of standards of care if it is viewed as valid and reproducible. This requires an ongoing auditing and feedback process and publication of data in order to effect practice changes.

Leape's work demonstrates that government and nongovernment organizations can advance the patient safety agenda. Some of the most effective organizations, such as the National Quality Forum, are quasi-governmental but rely on the widest possible array of stakeholders. A wonderful example of this is the Institute for Healthcare Improvement's national effort to reduce preventable deaths in U.S. hospitals. ● The campaign resulted in a truly exhilarating resurgence of spirit and an unprecedented commitment to change and collaboration across the healthcare industry. More than 3,100 participating hospitals achieved a remarkable goal by using the campaign's recommended interventions to save an estimated 122,000 lives in 18 months.

> ●
> The [IHI] campaign resulted in a truly exhilarating resurgence of spirit and an unprecedented commitment to change and collaboration across the healthcare industry.

The Role of Individuals

Both Leape and Hannan supported measures that were unpopular with their peers and within their fields. Separately, they helped build an evidence-based platform that could no longer be ignored. Monitoring and measuring the performance of individual providers, a touchy subject in the healthcare community, lie at the heart of improving quality and patient safety. Engaging providers in the process is important in order to ensure they make the necessary changes in their practices to improve healthcare quality and to guarantee safety. As Leape observes, patient-centered care must become the wave of the future.

While Leape and Hannan served as catalysts for change, it has been the voluntary efforts of many individuals wanting to do a better job — not out of fear or as a response to pressure from the government — that are improving quality and safety. Individuals can influence policy by their own actions, thus allowing government to play its role in facilitating that process by doing research, setting standards, and feeding data back that will, ultimately, shape policy.

Advocacy for Public Health Policy

For Leape, leadership is the art of getting other people to act on one's personal vision. He observes that there exists a conflict between the academic mission of his and other universities — namely, to advance knowledge and provide more understanding and thoughtful data — and the need for advocacy. In his view, when people in the public health community know useful information about public health issues, they are obligated to help inform the public and to play an active role in leading improvements.   ●   Leape says, "If you get good people talking about the right things, you'll get the right answers."

For Hannan, leadership is not only having a vision but also tempering it by figuring out ways to get it done. This means being attentive to colleagues who have good ideas and making sure that their ideas can be put into practice as well. As someone who works in the healthcare field but is not a medical doctor, Hannan sees the future of evidence-based medicine as an opportunity to compare the performance of providers and, by making this information public, to allow them to identify their own solutions that will improve quality of care delivered in hospitals.

Leape and Hannan have rejected the status quo of the healthcare industry and have shed light on the hidden secrets of medical errors and preventable death. Their work has led to the emergence of new standards of care. Healthcare will never be the same, and the work continues. ❀ ❀

●

"If you get good people talking about the right things, you'll get the right answers."

References

1. Robinson AR, Hohmann KB, Rifkin JI, Topp D, Gilroy CM, Pickard JA, Anderson RJ. Physicians and public opinions on quality of health care and the problem of medical errors. *Archives of Internal Medicine*. 2002 Oct 28; 162(19): 2186-2190.

2. Institute of Medicine. Crossing the quality chasm: a new health system for the 21st century. Washington, DC: National Academies Press; 2001.

3. Institute of Medicine. Crossing the quality chasm: a new health system for the 21st century. Washington, DC: National Academies Press; 2001.

4. Institute of Medicine. Crossing the quality chasm: a new health system for the 21st century. Washington, DC: National Academies Press; 2001.

5. Koo D; Centers for Disease Control and Prevention. Lecture. Overview of public health surveillance. [cited 2007 Aug 24]. Available from: http://www.pitt.edu/~super1/lecture/lec3011/003.htm.

6. West Virginia Department of Health and Human Resources [Home page on the Internet]. Charleston (WV): Principles of epidemiology. lesson 5 public health surveillance. [cited 2007 Aug 24]. Available from: http://www.wvdhhr.org/IDEP/PDFs/IDEP/Lesson5.pdf.

7. Schyve PM. An interview with Lucian Leape. Joint Commission on Quality and Safety. 2004; 30(12): 653-58.

8. Institute of Medicine. Crossing the quality chasm: a new health system for the 21st century. Washington, DC: National Academies Press; 2001.

9. Agency for Healthcare Research and Quality [Home page on the Internet]. Rockville (MD): The challenges and potential for assuring quality health care for 21st century. [cited 2007 Aug 24]. Available from: http://www.ahrq.gov/qual/21stcena.htm.

10. Robinson AR, Hohmann KB, Rifkin JI, Topp D, Gilroy CM, Pickard JA, Anderson RJ 2186-2190.

11. Robinson AR, Hohmann KB, Rifkin JI, Topp D, Gilroy CM, Pickard JA, Anderson RJ 2186-2190.

12. Creation of the "Lucian Leape Institute" at Annual National Patient Safety Congress [news release]. North Adams (MA): National Patient Safety Foundation. 2007 May 3. Available from: http://npsf.org/pr/pressrel/2007-05-3.php.

13. Institute of Medicine. Kohn LT, Corrigan JM, Donaldson MS, editors. To err is human: building a safer health system. Washington, DC: National Academies Press; 2000.

14. Institute of Medicine. [Home page on Internet]. Washington, DC: Report brief. patient safety: achieving a new standard for care. [published 2003 Nov; cited 2007 Aug 24]. Available from: http://www.iom.edu/Object.File/Master/27/174/PatientSafety-web.pdf.

15. Hannan, EL, Wu C, Ryan TJ, Bennett E, Culliford A, Gold JP, Hartman A, Isom OW, Jones RH, McNeil B, Rose EA, Subramanian, VA. Do hospitals and surgeons with higher coronary artery bypass graft surgery volumes still have lower risk-adjusted mortality rates? *Circulation*. 2003; 108(7): 795-801.

16. New York State Department of Health. Adult cardiac surgery in New York state 2002-2004. [published June 2006; cited 2007 Sept 7]. Available from: www.health.state.ny.us/diseases/cardiovascular/heart_disease/docs/cabg_2002-2004.pdf.

17. Hannan EL, Kilburn H Jr, O'Donnell JF, Lukacik G, Shields EP. Adult open heart surgery in New York state: an analysis of risk factors and hospital mortality rates. *Journal of the American Medical Association*. 1990; 264(21): 2768-2774.

18. Peterson ED, DeLong ER, Jollis JC, Muhlbaier LH, Mark DB. The effects of New York's bypass surgery provider profiling on access to care and patient outcomes in the elderly. *Journal of the American College of Cardiology*. 1998; 32(4): 993-999.

19. Hannan EL, Sarrazin MSV, Doran D, Rosenthal GE. Provider profiling and quality improvement efforts in coronary artery bypass graft surgery. *Medical Care*. 2003; 41:1164-1172.

20. (Sort of) Rating Hospitals. Editorial. *The New York Times*. [published 2007 June 26; cited 2007 Sept 10]. Available from: http://www.nytimes.com/2007/06/26/opinion/26tue2.html?ex=1340510400&en=f91439fcf74b8832&ei=5088&partner=rssnyt&emc=rss.

21. Hannan EL, Kumar D, Racz M, Siu AL, Chassin MR. New York state's cardiac surgery reporting system: four years later. *Annals of Thoracic Surgery*. 1994; 58(6): 1852-1857.

22. Hannan EL, Siu AL, Kumar D, Racz M, Pryor DB, Chassin MR. Assessment of coronary artery bypass graft surgery performance in New York: is there a bias against taking high-risk patients? *Medical Care*. 1997; 35(1):49-56.

23. Chassin MR, Hannan EL, Spencer FC. Improving the outcomes of coronary artery bypass surgery: New York's experience. 4th ed. *Cardiac Anesthesia*. WB Saunders Company; 1999, 1347-1360.

24. Hannan EL, Siu AL, Kumar D, Kilburn H Jr, Chassin MR. The decline in coronary artery bypass graft surgery mortality in New York state: the role of surgeon volume. *Journal of the American Medical Association*. 1995; 273(18): 209-213.

25. Hannan EL, Kilburn H Jr, Racz M, Shields E, Chassin MR. Improving the outcomes of coronary artery bypass surgery in New York state. *Journal of the American Medical Association*. 1994; 271(10):761-766.

26. Chassin MR, Hannan EL, DeBuono BA. Reporting medical outcomes publicly: benefits and hazards. *New England Journal of Medicine*. 1996; 334(6): 394-398.s

27. Hannan EL, Wu C, Bennett EV, Carlson RE, Culliford AT, Gold JP, Higgins RSD, Smith CR, Jones RH. A risk index for predicting – hospital mortality for cardiac valve surgery. *Annals of Thoracic Surgery.* 2007; 83: 921-930.

28. Hannan EL, Wu C, Bennett EV, Carlson RV, Culliford AT, Gold JP, Higgins RSD, Isom OW, Smith CR, Jones RH. Risk stratification of in-hospital mortality for coronary artery bypass graft surgery. *Journal of the American College of Cardiology.* 2006; 47: 661-668.

29. Wu C, Hannan EL,Walford G, Ambrose JA, Holmes DR Jr., King SB III, Clark LT, Katz S, Sharma S, Jones RH. A risk score to predict in-hospital mortality for percutaneous coronary interventions. *Journal of the American College of Cardiology.* 2006; 4: 654-660.

30. Hannan EL, Racz M, Kavey R-E, Quaegebeur JM, Williams R. Pediatric cardiac surgery: the effect of hospital and surgeon volume on in-hospital mortality. *Pediatrics.* 1998 June 6; 101(6): 963-969.

31. Hannan EL, Wu C, Walford G, King SB III, Holmes DR, Ambrose JA, Sharma S, Katz S, Clark LT, Jones RH. Volume-outcome relationships for percutaneous coronary interventions in the stent era. *Circulation.* 2005; 112: 1171-1179.

32. Wu C, Hannan EL, Ryan TJ, Bennett E, Culliford AT, Gold JP, Isom OW, Jones RH, McNeil B, Rose EA, Subramanian VA. Is the impact of hospital and surgeon volumes on in-hospital mortality rate for coronary artery bypass graft surgery limited to patients of high risk? *Circulation.* 2004; 110:784-789.

33. Hannan, EL, Wu C, Ryan TJ, Bennett E, Culliford A, Gold JP, Hartman A, Isom OW, Jones RH, McNeil B, Rose EA, Subramanian, VA. Do hospitals and surgeons with higher coronary artery bypass graft surgery volumes still have lower risk-adjusted mortality rates? *Circulation.* 2003; 108(7): 795-801. Epub 2003 July 28.

34. Hannan EL. The relation between volume and outcome in health care. Invited Editorial. *New England Journal of Medicine.* 1999; 56(3): 1677-1679.

35. Hannan EL. Percutaneous coronary interventions: heed the ACC volume recommendations, but strive to improve quality. Invited Editorial. *Journal of the American College of Cardiology.* 1999; 34(5):1481-1483.

36. Hannan EL, Kilburn H Jr, Bernard H, O'Donnell JF, Lukacik G, Shields EP. Coronary artery bypass surgery: the relationship between in-hospital mortality rate and surgical volume after controlling for clinical risk factors. *Medical Care.* 1991; 29(11):1094-1107.

37. Hannan EL, Racz M, Ryan TJ, McCallister BD, Johnson LW, Arani DT, Guerci AD, Sosa J, Topol EJ. Coronary angioplasty volume-outcome relationships for hospitals and cardiologists. *Journal of the American Medical Association.* 1997 March 19; 277(11): 892-898.

38 Hannan EL, van Ryn M, Burke J, Stone D, Kumar D, Arani D, Pierce W, Rafii S, Sanborn TA, Sharma S, Slater J, DeBuono BA. Access to coronary artery bypass surgery by race/ethnicity and gender among patients who are appropriate for surgery. *Medical Care.* 1999 Jan; 37(1): 68-77.

39. Hannan EL, Kilburn H Jr, O'Donnell JF, Lukacik G, Shields EP. Interracial access to selected cardiac procedures for patients hospitalized with coronary artery disease in New York state. *Medical Care.* 1991 May; 29(5): 430-441.

40. Hannan EL, Racz MJ, Walford G, Jones RH, Ryan TH, Bennett E, Culliford AT, Isom OW, Gold JP, Rose EA. Long-term outcomes for coronary artery bypass graft surgery versus stent implantation. *New England Journal of Medicine.* 2005 May 26; 352(21): 2174-2183.

41. Hannan EL, Racz MJ, McCallister BD, Ryan TJ, Arani DT, Isom OW, Jones RH. A comparison of three-year survival following coronary artery bypass graft surgery and percutaneous transluminal coronary angioplasty. *Journal of the American College of Cardiology.* 1999; 33: 63-72.

42. Hannan EL, Racz M, Holmes DR, King SB III, Walford G, Ambrose JA, Sharma S, Katz S, Clark LT, Jones RH. The impact of completeness of percutaneous coronary intervention revascularization on long-term outcomes in the stent era. *Circulation.* 2006; 113: 2406-2412. Epub 2006 May 15.

43. Hannan EL, Racz MJ, McCallister BD, Ryan TJ, Arani DT, Isom OW, Jones RH. A comparison of three-year survival following coronary artery bypass graft surgery and percutaneous transluminal coronary angioplasty. *Journal of the American College of Cardiology.* 1999; 33: 63-72.

44. Racz MA, Hannan EL, Isom OW, Subramanian VA, Jones RH, Gold JP, Ryan TJ, Hartman A, Culliford AT, Bennett E, Lancey RA, Rose EA. A comparison of short - and long-term outcomes following off-pump and on-pump coronary artery bypass graft surgery with sternotomy. *Journal of the American College of Cardiology.* 2004; 43: 557-564.

45. Hannan EL, Racz MJ, Arani DT, McCallister BD, Walford G, Ryan TJ. A comparison of short- and long-term outcomes for balloon angioplasty and coronary stent placement. *Journal of the American College of Cardiology.* 2000; 36: 395-403.

Chapter 5. **No Excuses:**

Reducing the Risk of Preventable Injury and Disease

Introduction

*W*ith so much media coverage about the dangers of disease and terrorism, it is surprising to know that unintentional injuries, or accidents, are the leading cause of death for people under the age of 35.[1] Injuries caused by risk-taking behaviors (such as riding a motorcycle without a helmet) or environmental threats (such as lead paint) challenge policymakers to create strategies that address individual and community behavioral change.

Injury is a significant public health problem that not only causes premature death and disability in Americans but also creates a burden on the healthcare system.[2] In 2000, more than 148,000 people in the United States died from injuries.[3] In addition, injuries accounted for 37 percent of visits to hospital emergency rooms.[4] The costs of injury are estimated to be more than $260 billion today;[5] federal, state, and local government funds cover 28 percent of medical expenditures,[6] and private sources cover the remaining 72 percent.[7]

●

These data have important policy implications because many of the risk factors leading to injuries can be modified or prevented through cost-effective interventions.

● These data have important policy implications because many of the risk factors leading to injuries can be modified or prevented through cost-effective interventions.[8] For example, an estimated 240,000 lives were saved between 1966 and 1990 as a result of improved motor vehicle and highway design, increased use of safety belts and motorcycle helmets, and enforcement of drinking and driving laws.

In June 1992, in an effort to reduce injuries and their costs, the Centers for Disease Control and Prevention (CDC) established the National Center for Injury Prevention and Control (NCIPC). In its role as the chief federal agency seeking to reduce injury throughout the United States, NCIPC works closely with other federal agencies; national, state, and local organizations; state and local health departments; and research institutions. In order to have a large-scale impact in communities, NCIPC also needs the support of nongovernmental organizations. Many have gained national stature promoting policy change in environment and injury. ● These nongovernmental organizations often have a surprising factor in common — the force of the personality and leadership qualities of the founders in driving environmental and injury policy change.

An example is Candy Lightner, who founded Mothers Against Drunk Driving (MADD) in 1980 after a repeat-offense drunken driver killed her 13-year-old daughter, Cari, in Fair Oaks, Calif.[9] MADD grew quickly in membership when legions of like-minded mothers, needing help to move beyond their personal tragedies, thronged to the organization. Fired by the passion of individuals demanding changes in public policies, MADD has helped pass thousands of enforceable laws against drunken driving and underage drinking. On the federal level, MADD pushed Congress to enact a law in 1984 mandating a minimum drinking age of 21, and to enact in 1995 the zero tolerance provision for those under 21, making it illegal to drive after consuming alcohol. In 2000, MADD also pushed Congress to pass a new federal limit of 0.08 percent blood alcohol concentration for drivers.[10]

MADD is but one example of individual advocacy that leads to legislation ushering in new public health policy. Another example is Marilyn Adams and the organization she founded called Farm Safety 4 Just Kids. Adams' 11-year-old son, Keith, died in 1986 when he fell into a gravity flow wagon while assisting his father with the corn harvest on their farm in Iowa. Sucked under, Keith suffocated. After a tailspin of grief, Adams rebounded to begin a model farm safety campaign, mobilizing community and public health leaders and legislators.

Environmental and injury-related legislation owes much to the passionate advocacy of people like Lightner and Adams. In relat-

●

These nongovernmental organizations often have a surprising factor in common — the force of the personality and leadership qualities of the founders in driving environmental and injury policy change.

ing powerful personal stories of tragedy, they gain followers, build organizations, and enable legislative and public health policy change. In fact, legislators often take action as a result of tragedies in their own families or among close friends.[11]

When the medical community joins forces with public health to advocate changes in the delivery of clinical care, policy changes begin to make their impact. An example is lead prevention and control. In 1978, an estimated 13.5 million children in the United States had elevated lead levels in their blood ($\geq 10\mu g/dL$).[12] Since the 1980s, the Environmental Protection Agency (EPA) and its federal partners have enforced regulations enacted by Congress that phased out lead in gasoline, reduced lead in drinking water and in industrial air pollution, and either banned or limited lead in consumer products, including paint.[13]

By 2002, the number of children in the U.S. with elevated lead levels in their blood dropped to 310,000 — less than 1 percent of the 1978 number, a remarkable reduction.[14] Limiting childhood exposure to lead, advancing clinical guidelines for lead screening and treatment, and improving access to care and coverage for children are the three main elements of public health policies that have helped eliminate an environmental threat and its clinical consequences.

●

Having the data, proposing solutions, and being tenacious are all necessary in order to influence policymakers to take the necessary steps to reduce the risk of injury and disease.

● Having the data, proposing solutions, and being tenacious are all necessary in order to influence policymakers to take the necessary steps to reduce the risk of injury and disease. One passionate advocate for environmental policy change is Patty Young, a flight attendant who was instrumental in eliminating smoking from airplanes. She became an agent of legislative and regulatory environmental change based on her personal experience of exposure to secondhand smoke.[15] Without her leadership and years of effort, flight attendants might still be risking their lives every day because of the unacceptable quality of airplane air. Former Surgeon General Julius Richmond observes that Young's long struggle against airline management, her own union, and the tobacco industry offers one of the most compelling examples of the ability of one person to effect sweeping change in public health.[16]

Another example of an individual's ability to create change is Abraham Bergman, MD, and his work in Seattle. His efforts to reduce injury among children, based on his clinical work as a pediatrician, continue to result in pivotal legislation. His well-aimed advocacy at the federal level helped Congress pass the National Sudden Infant Death Syndrome Act of 1974, the Poison Prevention Packaging Act of 1970, and the Flammable Fabrics Act of 1967, making children's clothing flame-retardant. Even more satisfying to Bergman, however, is his success in his home city of Seattle in encouraging young bicycle riders to wear safety helmets. A triumph of social marketing rather than coercive legislation, this effort is an example to many other large cities throughout the country of how to accomplish injury prevention.[17] ✿

National Case Study

Patty Young and Smoke-Free Airplanes

Patty Young

$\mathcal{T}$o meet Patty Young is to marvel at how one person, determined to confront a threat to the public's health while struggling to be heard against an array of powerful interests, can create change in public health policy. The banning of smoking on airplanes was her cause and transformed Young into a leading advocate for eliminating secondhand smoke exposure. To Young, smoking is an abomination that society should not tolerate on any level.

Young's story begins where she was raised, in the oil fields of Bakersfield, Calif. She remembers running to the local store with a note and a quarter to purchase a pack of cigarettes for her mother. Both of her parents were smokers, and both later died from lung cancer caused by smoking. She remembers the crinkly sound of the pack being opened, the match being struck, the first intake from the lit cigarette, and the seeming calmness that settled on her mother as she exhaled. ● She can think of no better proof that smoking is a socially acceptable form of drug addiction.

●

She can think of no better proof that smoking is a socially acceptable form of drug addiction.

When Young took her first airplane ride at 13 years of age, she knew instantly that she wanted to become a flight attendant. She saw that flight attendants travel the world without a boss hovering over their shoulders and are free from a nine-to-five existence. When she became a flight attendant at the age of 20, she had never been away from home nor had she ever dated. The world opened up for her.

Almost immediately, Young realized something was very wrong with cigarette smoking on airplanes. Many other flight attendants in their 20s and 30s who had never smoked told her that their doctors said they had the lungs of a smoker. In her case, she became ill with pounding headaches, irritated eyes, inflamed skin, chronic sinus infections, chronic bladder infections, vomiting, and diarrhea. After retiring from American Airlines in 2002 with 37 years of flying experience, she went into anaphylactic shock after having been exposed to heavy concentrations of secondhand smoke. At 60 years of age, she has chronic bronchitis and frequent laryngitis.

Young began her campaign to ban smoking on airplanes because it made sense. She says, "Everything I've ever done is just common sense, basic rule of thumb." Her campaign began as word of mouth. ● Six months after beginning her career as a flight attendant, she began suggesting to passengers who objected to cigarette smoke that they contact their senators and representatives in Congress. She found support among some of her fellow flight attendants but none from her union or the airline. Later, as she testified before congressional committees and advocated for a smoking ban directly to members of Congress, she found growing support among Democrats but met stiff resistance from Republicans. Young recalls one congressman having said, "I heard you were coming three days ago, what can I do to help you?" She replied, "You can either help me or fight me, because I'm not going anywhere."

● Six months after beginning her career as a flight attendant, [Young] began suggesting to passengers who objected to cigarette smoke that they contact their senators and representatives in Congress.

Young says, "I knew there was a movement from the very beginning. One thing I learned is that anecdotes always point to the truth." Once her seniority permitted it, she always flew Position I and stood at the entry door greeting every boarding passenger. In Position I, she met influential people who she thought would support her campaign. She recalls stuffing white towels into the return air vent above her. Later when she removed them, they were the color of dark coffee. When she wiped her face with a tissue, it would be the color of dark tea. When she navigated the aisle, the cloud of cigarette smoke could be so dense that she could not see to the back of the airplane. The clean clothes she packed in her travel suitcase would reek of tobacco smoke for an entire three-day trip.

Young's campaign began to turn in her favor when several airplanes crashed as a result of on-board fires started by lit cigarettes. In 1973, a Varig airliner made an emergency landing in Paris, ablaze from an out-of-control fire caused by a lit cigarette; all 124 passengers and crew perished. David Kennerly, later the official White House photographer for President Gerald Ford, happened to be at the scene and took photographs of an intact airplane with heavy black smoke billowing through windows that had been broken in the hope of escape. Not long after, Kennerly shared this experience with Young in Position I on one of his flights. They became friends, and she internalized the power of his story in her campaign to ban smoking.

In 1983, an Air Canada flight from Dallas to Toronto was forced to make an emergency landing in Cincinnati. A cigarette, carelessly extinguished in the lavatory trash bin by a woman who had been warned not to smoke in the nonsmoking section, had caused a fire. Half of the passengers perished from burns and toxic fumes. Young says, "I took that and used it as fuel personally and as fuel for this movement." ● Furthermore, she had to extinguish five on-board fires caused by burning cigarettes in the lavatories and in the seats. She also had to evacuate from three hotels while on layovers because of fires caused by lit cigarettes.

In 1973, the Civil Aeronautics Board (CAB) announced that all commercial airline flights would have smoking and nonsmoking sections. In 1984, the CAB announced in a national press conference that smoking on airplanes would be banned because it was a health and safety hazard and caused fatal crashes. Young remembers seeing the announcement on television and shouting so loudly and leaping so high that her dogs ran outside. She also recalls watching Peter Jennings later in the same news program accept a passed piece of paper and announce that smoking would not be banned after all. That was a temporary setback, however, because overwhelming evidence of the ill effects of secondhand smoke and the hazards caused by cigarettes on airplanes continued to mount.

●

Furthermore, [Young] had to extinguish five on-board fires caused by burning cigarettes in the lavatories and in the seats. She also had to evacuate from three hotels while on layovers because of fires caused by lit cigarettes.

Young testified before congressional committees three times about banning smoking on airplanes. She remembers that some of the committee members and the spectators in the hearing room deliberately were lighting up and smoking nonstop. She took that as a sign that her work was not going to be easy and that "You had to talk to anybody who would listen." ● She says, "This has nothing to do with heroes; this is about being a street-fighter and doing the right thing." Statistics show that when California and New York City went smoke-free — banning smoking from most businesses, including restaurants, bars, bowling alleys, dance clubs, and pool halls, and furthering the social stigma of secondhand smoke — more than 10 percent of smokers quit in the first year. Young believes that the Americans With Disabilities Act and the Rehabilitation Act of 1973 can stop smoking in workplaces, public buildings, and public accommodations in the United States. She used these acts to get Dallas-Ft. Worth airport smoke-free in 1993 and then Love Field in 1994. She knows firsthand that these acts can be used to impose smoking restrictions in public indoor spaces and wonders when more activists and public health groups will jump on board.

●

"This has nothing to do with heroes; this is about being a street-fighter and doing the right thing."

On June 2, 1997, the very day that American Airlines announced that all flights, domestic and international, would be smoke-free, a class action suit brought on behalf of nonsmoking flight attendants with chronic health problems went to trial. The suit, first filed in October 1991, alleged that exposure to secondhand smoke in airline cabins caused chronic health problems. Flight attendants had the highest rates of breast cancer of any other group in the country, had elevated rates of throat cancer, and were dying from lung cancer at ages as young as 28. Young had extreme difficulty finding lawyers to file the lawsuit for the willful disregard of the health and safety of the flight attendants, but her persistence paid off.

After trying for more than two decades, Young was referred to Stanley and Susan Rosenblatt, a husband and wife legal team in Miami, Fla. To Young, these attorneys are the real heroes. They put everything on the line to undertake the litigation because it was the right thing to do. As the parents of nine children, one a newborn at the time, they toiled for six years to get the case before a jury to seek justice for the injured nonsmoking flight attendants. According to Young, the case is extraordinary because it was the first class action suit against tobacco companies, one of the first lawsuits against the industry and the first for secondhand smoke. The litigation also hastened banning smoking on all international flights, which had escaped the outright bans on domestic flights.

When Phase I of the suit was settled in October 1997, the Flight Attendant Medical Research Institute (FAMRI) was formed as part of the broad settlement and began to function several years later when all appeals were over and the $300 million settlement had been paid. Phase 2 is still being litigated. This litigation has finally put faces on the flight attendants who were victims of tobacco companies and recalcitrant airline companies. FAMRI now gives hope for cures to flight attendants who are fighting the diseases caused by unacceptable air quality on airlines.

By virtue of her nonstop, word-of-mouth campaign during which she gained support from many other health and anti-tobacco groups and citizens, ● Young gradually wore down resistance to banning smoking on airplanes from her airline, the union, Congress, and federal agencies. Along the way, a handful of special flight attendants that cared about this issue put their jobs on the line, joined her campaign, and worked very hard. It was the threat of monetary damages, however, that finally made airline companies relent and make airplanes smoke-free on domestic flights. ✺

●

Young gradually wore down resistance to banning smoking on airplanes from her airline, the union, Congress, and federal agencies.

Local Case Study

Abraham Bergman
and Bicycle Helmets in Seattle

*F*or Abraham Bergman, MD, the campaign in Seattle to get young bicycle riders to wear safety helmets is just one triumph in the many injury-prevention campaigns he has waged. Too many ambulances carrying too many patients with critical injuries caused him to become a leading proponent of injury prevention. After having helped treat numerous children with serious head injuries caused by bicycle accidents, Bergman began a campaign in Seattle in the early 1980s with his colleague, Dr. Fred Rivara, to motivate children to wear helmets. A case control study done by colleagues at the Harborview Injury Prevention and Research Center showed the protective effects of bicycle helmets to be 85 percent.[18] Young children, rather than resistant teenagers or adults set in their ways, were the targets of the campaign.

Abraham Bergman, MD

Bergman, a Seattle native, was educated at Reed College in Portland, Ore., and at Western Reserve University Medical School in Cleveland, Ohio. Later, he trained in pediatrics at Boston Children's Hospital. While he has fought all of his campaigns for injury prevention on his home turf, many have had national implications thanks to his strong working relationship with (now deceased) Sen. Warren Magnuson of Washington State, the longtime chair of the Senate Appropriations Subcommittee overseeing health spending. The campaigns all started simply from Bergman's clinical experiences as a pediatrician, first at Children's Hospital in Seattle and later at Harborview Medical Center, the largest public hospital in the Pacific Northwest. Currently, he is involved with creating a play garden in south-central Seattle to serve developmentally and physically impaired youngsters.

Bergman faced three critical hurdles in his campaign to get child bicyclists to wear safety helmets. First, parents had to be convinced that helmets were needed. Second, the price had to be affordable. Third, children riding bicycles, an activity with inherent risks, had to look beyond the "nerd factor" and embrace a look that protected their heads.

Bergman says, "I like to use motivation rather than education. How do you get people to do things? The masters of that are advertising people. They create a market." He had a natural publicity engine at Harborview, the only Level I trauma center in the huge four-state area of Washington, Alaska, Montana, and Idaho. Local news crews were thirsty for stories about trauma victims. If the message was repeated often enough and reached a wide enough audience that wearing bicycle helmets could prevent the permanent brain damage resulting from falls, then behavior change might stand a chance of success. ● Interviews with seriously injured children and parents broadcast by local news crews had a powerful effect in stimulating helmet use.

●

Interviews with seriously injured children and parents broadcast by local news crews had a powerful effect in stimulating helmet use.

Another challenge was the cost of safety helmets, which at that time were available only in specialty stores and cost between $60 and $80, as much as a starter bicycle itself. Fortunately, strategies fell into place to help counter this phenomenon. A small manufacturer in Seattle of high-end equipment for mountain climbing, Mountain Safety Research, thought that low-cost helmets were a great idea. The company, led by a cyclist, arranged to manufacture low-cost helmets in Taiwan and to sell them in Seattle for $15 each through Fred Meyer, a large northwestern retailer. Bergman arranged for Fred Meyer stores to receive a Corporation Good Citizen award from the Washington Chapter of the American Academy of Pediatrics in recognition of their efforts.

He next approached Toys "R" Us, the largest toy retailer in the United States at that time. Calling on the 28-year-old buyer for bicycles, who had been on the job for several months, Bergman gained agreement to promote the sale of a $20 helmet with every bicycle sold. Toys "R" Us arranged for the manufacturing through a family business in San Diego called Troxel, led by a critical care physician. Very quickly, other manufacturers jumped in, and bicycle safety helmets can now be purchased for approximately $15 nationwide.

Seattle has one of the largest cycling communities in the country, and Bergman formed a coalition of safety experts, leaders in the cycling community, and physicians to educate children and their parents about the importance of wearing helmets. They created momentum for the campaign by conducting clinics led by cyclists with Spider-Man as an attraction. They also taped public service announcements with Seattle Mariners players and had local McDonald's give away free french fries and hold lotteries for free Mariners tickets.

Evaluating the success of the campaign, Bergman and Rivara compared statistics in Seattle with those in Portland. Both cities began with three percent compliance in wearing safety helmets. While Portland rose to 12 percent, Seattle soared to 65 percent.[19] This was without legislation. Bergman says, ● "I am dubious of legislation without a promotional campaign. Cops don't like to give tickets to 8-year-olds."

He observes, "In general, getting money for injury prevention is difficult because it's not sexy. Victims don't band together, so that's a problem." Getting the bicycle helmet campaign in Seattle to the critical mass required a full-time coordinator, and for two years there wasn't one, because of the expense. Once a coordinator was named, the campaign took off. While in-kind contributions by the cycling community, graphic artists, physicians, and even the Seattle Mariners were critical to the campaign's success, the position of campaign coordinator, relatively inexpensive, was the most critical contribution of all. ✱

●

"I am dubious of legislation without a promotional campaign. Cops don't like to give tickets to 8-year-olds."

Lessons Learned

Young and Bergman have deep personal views of what leadership is all about. Young says, "It means that individuals can take their anger and turn it into something that is positive to stop something that is wrong or change status-quo thinking. If we can't see the tobacco issue as the most important issue of peace and the most obscene issue the world has ever seen, we're not going to do anything to save humanity and our world. Every bit of it is interconnected."

Bergman knows that the pitfalls of being in a leadership position include administrative issues. He says, "Too many advocates for children get lost in the process and lose sight of the results. They get taken in by the crowd noise, the number of meetings held, the letters written. I care only about crossing the goal line, that's all. One either wins or loses; all the stuff in between is irrelevant." He adds, "Charisma, having the vision and the energy, and selling it to people and then inspiring them is leadership." He concludes, "You don't need organizations; you need individuals and one person who steps up to say, 'Let's get it done.'"

> "You don't need organizations; you need individuals and one person who steps up to say, 'Let's get it done.'"

There are important lessons to be learned from the examples of Young and Bergman.

The Role of Public Health in Policy

Public health improvement and policy change cannot be separated from clinical medicine. Most of the issues in injury prevention and the consequences of risk-taking behaviors and environmental threats arise directly from observations of clinicians in treating patients. This was the case for Bergman who, as a pediatrician, took action after having seen too many children end up in the hospital with serious, yet preventable, injuries. For Young, it was observations about her own health that made the link between her workplace environment — an airplane cabin — and secondhand smoke. While both Young's and Bergman's campaigns arose from personal experiences, their work has contributed greatly to the improvement of the public's health.

Sound Policy Analysis in Public Health Practice

Young's and Bergman's accomplishments demonstrate that influencing policymakers requires having the data, proposing solutions, and being tenacious. Although not a public health professional herself, Young presented convincingly, and from firsthand experience, the overwhelming evidence of the ill effects of secondhand smoke and the hazards caused by cigarettes on airplanes. ● Her battle took years, and whenever new evidence became available that supported her cause, she wasted no time in talking publicly and loudly about it.

●

[Young's] battle took years, and whenever new evidence became available that supported her cause, she wasted no time in talking publicly and loudly about it.

Bergman knew that legislating bicycle helmet use would be unpopular with citizens and law enforcement. Instead, he looked at the potential barriers to wider helmet use — the design, cost, and availability — and created interesting partnerships that provided solutions. Once the campaign was in place, he and his colleagues were able to show that their bicycle safety helmet campaign was taking hold when compliance in Seattle soared to 65 percent, and by comparison, Portland's rose to only 12 percent.

The Role of Individuals

Young and Bergman, two individuals who have had a profound impact on creating policies that address disease and injury risk reduction, share a leadership characteristic that is critical to success — setting goals and doing everything possible to achieve them. Each one views his and her own public health campaigns as, first and foremost, the act of an individual committed to changing policies to protect the health of the public.

While they formed coalitions with like-minded organizations and enlisted supporters for their cause, they acted first as individuals, strongly motivated to enact change. Their singular passions, found deep within themselves, had the most to do with their successes.

Advocacy for Public Health Policy

Even though Young and Bergman have successfully advocated for legislation, they view social marketing as equally important in preventing injury and environmental harm. ● Social marketing works when the activity to be prevented — smoking on airplanes, riding bicycles without head protection — begins to be viewed as a social stigma.

●
Social marketing works when the activity to be prevented — smoking on airplanes, riding bicycles without head protection — begins to be viewed as a social stigma.

Establishing nonsmoking sections on aircraft began a broad movement that put a social stigma on smoking, leading over time to smoke-free indoor spaces. Encouraging young bicyclists to wear safety helmets, just as with safety seats and seat belts in automobiles, gains a following because it makes sense. When children start something young, they stick with it. Wearing a seat belt or bicycle helmet becomes a routine behavior and a social norm.

Young and Bergman elegantly demonstrate that personal motivation and experience, coupled with a deep understanding of solutions that will work, often make the difference in changing public health policy. ❀ ❀

References

1. CDC/National Center for Health Statistics. NCHS data on injury. [updated 2006 June 30; cited 2007 Sep 17]. Available from: http://www.cdc.gov/nchs/data/factsheets/injury.pdf.

2. Centers for Disease Control and Prevention [Home page on the Internet]. Atlanta: About CDC's injury center. [updated 2007 July 5; cited 2007 Aug 24]. Available from: http://www.cdc.gov/ncipc/about/about.htm.

3. Centers for Disease Control and Prevention [Home page on the Internet]. Atlanta: About CDC's injury center. [updated 2007 July 5; cited 2007 Aug 24]. Available from: http://www.cdc.gov/ncipc/about/about.htm.

4. Pastor PN, Makuc DM, Reuben C, Xia H. Chartbook on Trends in the Health of Americans. Health, United States, 2002. Hyattsville, MD: National Center for Health Statistics. 2002.

5. Corrigan JM, Donaldson MS, Kohn LT, McKay T, Pike KC for the Committee on Quality of Health Care in America. To err is human: building a safer health system. Washington, D.C.: National Academies Press; 2000. [cited 2003 June 27]. Available at: http://books.nap.edu/catalog/9728.html.

6. Centers for Disease Control and Prevention [Home page on the Internet]. Atlanta: About CDC's injury center. [updated 2007 July 5; cited 2007 Aug 24]. Available from: http://www.cdc.gov/ncipc/about/about.htm.

7. Rice DP, MacKenzie EJ and Associates. Cost of injury in the United States: a report to congress, 1989. San Francisco, CA: Institute for Health & Aging, University of California and Injury Prevention Center, The Johns Hopkins University. 1989.

8. Pruss-Ustan A, Corvalan C.; World Health Organization. Preventing disease through healthy environments: towards an estimate of the environmental burden of the disease. Geneva: WHO Press; 2006. Available from: http://www.who.int/quantifying_ehimpacts/publications/preventingdisease/en/index.html.

9. Mothers Against Drunk Driving (MADD) [Home page on the Internet]. Irving (TX): Who founded MADD? [cited 2007 Aug 24]. Available from: http://www.madd.org/aboutus/1195.

10. Mothers Against Drunk Driving (MADD) [Home page on the Internet]. Irving (TX): MADD quick profile. [cited 2007 Aug 24]. Available from: http://www.madd.org/aboutus/1180.

11. Levenstein C. Flight attendant's role in success of smoking ban. Electronic letters to Holme A and Davis RM. Clearing the airways: advocacy and regulation for smoke-free airlines. *Tobacco Control*, 2004: 13: 30i-36i.

12. United States Environmental Protection Agency [Home page on the Internet]. Washington, DC: Lead awareness program: protect your child from lead poisoning. [updated 2007 Aug 2; cited 2007 Aug 24]. Available from: http://www.epa.gov/lead/.

13. United States Environmental Protection Agency [Home page on the Internet]. Washington, DC: Lead awareness program: protect your child from lead poisoning. [updated 2007 Aug 2; cited 2007 Aug 24]. Available from: http://www.epa.gov/lead/.

14. United States Environmental Protection Agency [Home page on the Internet]. Washington, DC: Lead awareness program: protect your child from lead poisoning. [updated 2007 Aug 2; cited 2007 Aug 24]. Available from: http://www.epa.gov/lead/.

15. Richmond JB, Burns DM, Cummings KM. Public health and the power of individual action. *Tobacco Control*. 2004; 13: 1-2.

16. Richmond JB, Burns DM, Cummings KM. Public health and the power of individual action. *Tobacco Control*. 2004; 13: 1-2.

17. Renowned US child advocate to discuss political medicine at Oberlin April 28. [news release]. Oberlin (OH): Oberlin College News Services; 2000 Apr 17. Available from: http://www.oberlin.edu/newserv/stories/bergman_release.html.

18. Thompson DC, Rivara FP, Thompson RS. Effectiveness of bicycle safety helmets in preventing head injuries. A case-control study. *Journal of American Medical Association*. 1996 Dec 25; 276(24): 1968-1973.

19. Bergman AB, Rivara FP, Richards DD, Rogers LW. The Seattle children's bicycle helmet campaign. *American Journal of Diseases of Children*. 1990 Jun; 144(6): 727-731.

Chapter 6.   **Choosing Health:**

Improving Individual and Community Health Through Health Promotion Strategies

Introduction

*I*t can be difficult to understand how one individual's health and safety choices can affect the entire population. However, if one thinks about smoking in public places or driving under the influence of alcohol, the connection becomes clear. Trying to change behavior in individuals as a means to improve the overall health of populations is known as *health promotion.* It is an integral function of public health and policymaking. In some cases, policies are developed to change behavior either through incentives or direct interventions in the choices that individuals make. Regulating the use of seat belts in cars and banning smoking in public places are examples of laws that affect behavior as a way to promote the health of the entire population.

Similarly, policy can be a means of eliminating broader barriers that prevent people from engaging in behaviors that promote health. For example, there is a strong correlation between the use of preventive pediatric healthcare and having health insurance coverage. There is also extensive evidence showing that low-income families do not use healthcare that is unaffordable. Laws designed to make affordable health insurance coverage available can have a significant impact on a family's ability to secure coverage, access preventive care, and use health services appropriately.

Health promotion works when people take action: improving their nutrition; increasing physical activity; avoiding the use of tobacco, alcohol, and other drugs; seeking help with family planning and mental health issues; controlling violent and abusive behavior; and gaining access to educational and community-based programs.[1] When individuals implement these behaviors, others and the health of the community benefit. Since each of these actions requires behavioral change, health promotion relies on incentives and regulatory powers that shape health policies, as well as on new technologies and services.[2] For example, to prevent lung cancer or reduce the prevalence of asthma, the public health community offers a variety of measures: controlling access to cigarettes, education about the dangers of smoking, making indoor environments smoke-free, and offering smoking cessation programs.[3] When health promotion works, public health measures guide not only individuals to change their behaviors but also communities, government personnel, and policymakers.

●   Policymaking in the area of population health often rests on a strong understanding of the relationship between individual behavioral choice and the broader social environment in which such individual choices take place. Health promotion can also yield broader externalities, that is, cost benefits for communities, states, and the nation. This aspect of health policymaking can act as a powerful incentive for policymakers whose main concern may be the high cost of healthcare and the excessive rate of health expenditures on illnesses and disabilities. Indeed, some of the advances in maternal and child health policy over the past generation rest on the notion of investing in children and families now as a means of avoiding long-term care costs later.

For policy leaders to be effective in promoting health, they must do more than educate the public. The great leaders in this area identify policies that contribute to individual and population health, as well as the broader social policies that affect the ability of individuals to choose health. They persuade policymakers to advance a legislative and regulatory agenda that strengthens the conditions in which people can be healthy. Examples include legislation requiring the use of seat belts and bicycle helmets and prohibiting smoking in public places, such as airports. The interaction between public health experts and policymakers is crucial to advancing health policy not only through legislation but also through broader fiscal policies and organizational change. It is

●

Policymaking in the area of population health often rests on a strong understanding of the relationship between individual behavioral choice and the broader social environment in which such individual choices take place.

essential that policymakers understand the role of policy in enabling people to choose health and that policies be developed with behavior in mind.[4]

This chapter examines the actions of Julius Richmond, MD, MS, the U.S. Surgeon General during the Carter Administration in the 1970s, and the former director of Head Start and Neighborhood (now Community) Health Centers in the Office of Economic Opportunity (OEO) during the Johnson Administration in the 1960s. ● The ongoing publication he initiated in 1979, called *Healthy People*, achieved consensus on quantified goals for the health of the entire population and changed the face of health promotion in the United States. This chapter also explores the actions of Joseph Thompson, MD, MPH, in Arkansas, where he initiated a body mass index (BMI) assessment as one element of a state-mandated, multipronged approach to the childhood obesity epidemic. Richmond's leadership at the federal level gained wide acceptance for a transformative report, pushing health promotion to the forefront of public health. Thompson, at the state level, has been working with schools throughout Arkansas to implement a legislated policy to derive immediate public health benefits. His leadership offers an example of an emerging health promotion policy that can become equally transforming at the national level. ❁

●

The ongoing publication [Richmond] initiated in 1979, called *Healthy People*, achieved consensus on quantified goals for the health of the entire population and changed the face of health promotion in the United States.

National Case Study

Julius Richmond and the
Healthy People Report

$\mathcal{P}$olicy leadership of health promotion in the United States
starts with the Office of the Surgeon General (OSG) and the
Public Health Service. Under Dr. Richmond's leadership,
prevention became the mission of the Public Health Service and
his *Healthy People* reports began to establish tangible goals for public
health. Tracing its origins to 1870, the Office of the Surgeon
General evolved from the Marine Hospital Service, a centralized
national hospital system. Its first supervising surgeon, Dr. John
Woodworth, was named in 1871.[5] Nearly a century later in 1968,
President Lyndon B. Johnson envisioned a new role for prevention
in what would become the U.S. Public Health Service (PHS).
Under President Johnson, the Surgeon General became the
principal deputy to the Assistant Secretary for Health within
what is now called the Department of Health and Human
Services (HHS), and is responsible for advising and assisting
with professional medical matters. The Surgeon General also
became the PHS spokesperson on certain health issues. In 1987,
the OSG became a staff office within the Office of the Assistant
Secretary for Health.[6]

*Julius Richmond,
MD, MS*

As President Johnson had envisioned, the OSG dramatically
influenced health promotion. Johnson's vision arose, in part,
from his own bout with heart disease. After years of smoking,
he had suffered a serious heart attack while serving as majority
leader of the U.S. Senate. His vision also owed much to the
efforts of President John F. Kennedy's Surgeon General, Luther
Terry, who established and chaired the Surgeon General's Advisory
Committee on Smoking and Health that produced what is now
commonly called the First Surgeon General's Report. Released on
January 11, 1964, the report established the significant and causal
link between cigarette smoking and lung cancer and chronic

bronchitis. This landmark report greatly increased concern about tobacco use among the American public and government policy-makers and led to a broad-based anti-smoking campaign. Despite a strong campaign by the tobacco industry to derail the report by questioning the link between smoking and disease, Congress passed the Cigarette Labeling and Advertising Act of 1965. The most familiar outcome of that act is the Surgeon General's health warning that appears on every pack of cigarettes.[7]

Nearly a decade later, during the administration of President Jimmy Carter, HEW Secretary Joseph Califano and Assistant Secretary of Health and Surgeon General Julius Richmond built on the 1960s precedent, creating consensus that prevention should be a central mission of the PHS. Richmond remains best-known for his leadership in devising and implementing quantitative goals for public health, first published as a report in 1979 called *Healthy People: the Surgeon General's Report on Health Promotion and Disease Prevention.* Popularly known as *Healthy People*, the PHS report spurred change by informing journalists, health departments, and the public about gains already made in reducing mortality from noninfectious causes.[8]

Richmond understood that health promotion is a set of processes that, when shared widely and wisely, can change the conditions that affect health. The 1979 report was remarkably successful in introducing the concept of health promotion to the nation.[9] It withstood political firestorms in Congress and the antagonism of the tobacco industry. In fact, Califano's outspoken criticism of cigarette smoking as a major contributor to prevent-able disease became the face of the report in the public's mind.[10] Although Califano departed halfway through President Carter's term, Richmond remained until 1981, the beginning of the Reagan administration.

Richmond came to the Surgeon General's office after a distin-guished career in pediatric medicine. Born and raised in Chicago, he received his undergraduate and medical education at the University of Illinois (spending two years in Urbana before completing his Bachelor of Science, Master of Science, and Doctor of Medicine degrees within two years at the medical campus in Chicago) and began a residency at Cook County Hospital. World War II and military service as a flight surgeon in the Army Air Corps interrupted his residency. Completing it after the war, Richmond joined the Department of Pediatrics at the University of Illinois Medical Center in Chicago. There, he led efforts to reform the medical school curriculum by integrating teaching across departments, promoting earlier patient contact, stressing psychological and social factors in health and illness, and emphasizing disease prevention and health maintenance. Although he gained unanimous backing for his ideas from the curriculum committee, the faculty vote soundly defeated the proposals. This led him to move the following year to Syracuse, N.Y., to become chief of pediatrics at the State University of New York Upstate Medical Center. There, he was able to put into practice many of his ideas about medical school curricula. He also teamed with psychologist Dr. Bettye Caldwell to found a precursor to the Head Start program.

During his childhood, Richmond discovered a motivation to address the needs of children, especially those less fortunate than himself. His parents, immigrants from czarist Russia, introduced him to Hull House in Chicago, an association founded by Jane Addams that improves social conditions for underserved people and communities, and he was impressed by the work carried out there by child advocates and reformers. After his mother died when he was 10 years old, he spent three years at Allendale, a boarding school for dependent boys. The school's founder, "Captain" Edward Bradley, furthered his interest in social justice. Richmond graduated from John Marshall High School in Chicago, and in 1933, he entered the University of Illinois in Urbana. There, he joined with like-minded students to demonstrate against segregated student housing. In medical school, located amid the terrible poverty of Chicago's West Side, he organized the Association of Medical Students to discuss social issues. At Cook County Hospital, he faced daily the privations of children whose poor health outcomes often resulted from impoverished social conditions. He had observed in the Army Air Corps that his fellow corpsmen went through tough emotional and mental adjustments. If the cream of the crop had such problems with psychosocial adjustment, he imagined that someone from a disadvantaged background would fare much worse. ● He realized that securing the best possible foundation for every child was the only way to ensure that as adults they would be able to seize the opportunities offered by society.

● [Richmond] realized that securing the best possible foundation for every child was the only way to ensure that as adults they would be able to seize the opportunities offered by society.

Before becoming Surgeon General in the Carter administration, Richmond served as the first director of Head Start and director of the Neighborhood Health Centers program within the Office of Economic Opportunity (OEO) in the Johnson administration. In overseeing the Neighborhood Health Centers program, he approved the first two health centers, one in the Columbia Point neighborhood of Boston and one in rural Bolivar County, Miss., proposed by Drs. Jack Geiger and Count Gibson of the School of Medicine at Tufts University. *(See case study on Geiger and Community Health Center Movement in Chapter 1.)*

In the Head Start position, Richmond addressed directly, on a national scale, the psychosocial development issues in children that he and Caldwell had researched in Syracuse. Relying on the knowledge base provided by Dr. Milton J.E. Senn of the Yale Child Study Center in New Haven, he and Caldwell discovered that most infants thrive as newborns, but by the time children in poverty become toddlers, serious developmental delays begin and then accelerate. The genesis of Head Start was their belief that for children in poverty, intervention had to begin before school age. The program they had begun in Syracuse gained the attention of Sargent Shriver, head of the OEO, who was committed to finding new ways to combat mental retardation through the Kennedy Foundation. It was a revelation to Shriver that the program Richmond and Caldwell had started in Syracuse had proved that environmental influences, as much as organic causes, could lead to developmental delays.

Thanks to Richmond's unflagging strategic sense, Head Start became an instant success. In June 1965, less than six months after he had arrived at the OEO, more than 2,700 sites opened across the country for an eight-week summer session. Richmond chose not to delay the opening for construction of classrooms and made use instead of existing structures and elementary school teachers during their summer breaks. As he says, ● "I tell students that when there is an opportunity to do something on a grand scale, you have to grab it and pitch in, but be sure it's got a good social strategy." Indeed, more than 24 million children have been served by Head Start since its inception. In 2006, a budget of $6.7 billion covered a staff of 218,000 and 1,365,000 volunteers, who served 909,201 children at a cost of $7,209 per child. Of the children served, 12.1 percent had disabilities such as mental retardation.

The *Healthy People* reports were born under Richmond's leadership, beginning with the first report in 1979. He recognized that the knowledge base had improved dramatically since his residency years in Chicago and that the political will for change was there. President Carter, as governor of Georgia, had implemented a statewide program in prevention and health promotion. What was needed now at the federal level was a social strategy. Richmond believed that the publication of a report summarizing the population's health status would begin to change behavior if widely reported in the media. In other words, the report itself could be transformational and reinforce health promotion as a central focus of federal public health policy.

Assistant Surgeon General Michael McGinnis oversaw the formal publication of the 1979 report from within a new Office of Disease Prevention and Health Promotion. The report's ambitious health goals, which were supposed to be achieved by 1990, were further refined in 1980 by an Institute of Medicine publication called *Promoting Health/Preventing Disease: Objectives for the Nation.* This volume established a series of specific targets to be achieved by 1990 within health categories for each age group.

●
"I tell students that when there is an opportunity to do something on a grand scale, you have to grab it and pitch in, but be sure it's got a good social strategy."

Educating people on how they could take more personal responsibility for their health through wise lifestyle choices became a
major goal of both reports.[11] As Richmond had hoped, the
substance of the reports gained widespread media attention, and
slowly individual health behaviors began to change. At the time
of the report, for example, the infant mortality rate was 12 per
1,000. The goal for 1990 was nine per 1,000 ("9 by 90"),
and this objective was, in fact, met.

Dr. David Satcher, sworn in as the 16th Surgeon General in 1998,[12]
published *Healthy People 2010* in 2000 to build on the many initiatives outlined in the 1979 report and its successor, *Healthy People
2000*. Like its predecessors, *Healthy People 2010* relied on a broad
consultation process, capturing the best scientific knowledge and
designing a measurement component.[13] Richmond explains that
the 10-year window he chose, essentially establishing health goals
for a decade, is a sufficient time span for vital statistics to be
measured and for goals to be meaningful. Just as resources were
never an issue with Congress during the War on Poverty initiatives
during the 1960s, they were not for *Healthy People* during the Carter
and subsequent administrations. Richmond knew that it was
important that the reporting process become institutionalized.
In fact, the reports gained such favorable publicity that health
ministries around the world have tried institutionalizing their own
goal-setting processes.

In fact, the
reports gained
such favorable
publicity that
health ministries
around the world
have tried institu-
tionalizing their
own goal-setting
processes.

During his term as Surgeon General, Richmond observed the 15th
anniversary of the First Surgeon General's Report by issuing an
anniversary report on the exact date, Jan. 11, 1979. The summary
of scientific data by this time had become overwhelming, and
Richmond wanted journalists to know that the data were very
abundant. The report effectively sent the tobacco industry into a
tailspin from which it has never recovered. Following decades in
which tobacco use in the population had shown steady increases,
the pattern reversed after the release of the First Surgeon General's
Report in 1964. Each succeeding decade has shown a decline in
tobacco use in the U.S. population. The Surgeon General's

report on secondhand smoke, issued by Dr. Everett Koop during the Reagan administration, and the movement toward smoke-free indoor spaces demonstrate the power of attainable health goals, backed by scientific data, in gaining support from the public and policymakers. The cumulative effect of the Surgeon General's reports and *Healthy People* is to convince health professionals, and especially physicians, that the evidence base on prevention is robust and well worth following.

● Despite the many Surgeon General reports and *Healthy People* reports over the past decades, complete support for health promotion is still a work in progress. The Centers for Disease Control and Prevention's (CDC) partnership with state and local health departments enhances prevention, and thus health promotion, in specific health categories.[14] Among the best-known CDC activities are a national behavioral risk factor and surveillance system, the Behavioral Sciences Working Group, and the Public Health Education and Promotion Network (PHEP Net). Professional development and work force development also have become key CDC activities. The CDC is also the driver for technical assistance and support to community-based health promotion programs. In monitoring and evaluating these programs, the CDC shares documented best practices, conducts training workshops, and develops Web sites. The CDC also supports research into the science, methodology, and process of community-based health education and health promotion programs.

Richmond decided on a successful social strategy — the *Healthy People* report issued on a repeating 10-year cycle — to jump start health promotion policy at the federal level. As he points out, neither the ever-expanding prevention knowledge base nor political power is sufficient to change behavior. Individual behavioral change happens when policymakers link an effective social strategy with an accepted health promotion policy. Pursuing just such a strategy, Joseph Thompson, MD, MPH, put Richmond's advice into practice in his home state of Arkansas. ❁

●

Despite the many Surgeon General reports and *Healthy People* reports over the past decades, complete support for health promotion is still a work in progress.

Local Case Study

Joseph Thompson and the Body Mass Index Assessment Project in Arkansas

Joseph Thompson, MD, MPH

*A*ddressing childhood obesity head-on has been the mission of Joseph Thompson, MD, MPH, director of the Arkansas Center for Health Improvement (ACHI) since 2003. Aside from stints in Washington, D.C., and North Carolina, Thompson has spent his entire career in his home state of Arkansas. A graduate of Hendrix College and the University of Arkansas for Medical Sciences (UAMS) at Little Rock, he also earned a Master of Public Health degree at the University of North Carolina at Chapel Hill in epidemiology and served as a Luther Terry Fellow in Washington, D.C., in the assistant secretary of health's office for Disease Prevention and Health Promotion. He also worked at the National Committee of Quality Assurance as research director, developing performance indicators for managed care and monitoring issues of quality. After he returned to Little Rock, he also served as a child health scholar with the Agency for Healthcare Research and Quality. He is double board certified in pediatrics and preventive medicine, with applicable expertise throughout the age spectrum. While Thompson was a practicing pediatrician at Arkansas Children's Hospital, he discovered that what he liked best was to be in the center where the circles of clinical care, public health, and health policy overlap.

Thompson serves as Surgeon General of Arkansas, a cabinet level advisory position to the governor. In that role, he coordinates closely with Paul Halverson, director of the Arkansas Department of Health. The men attended the University of North Carolina at Chapel Hill together to earn their MPH degrees and enjoy a close professional working relationship.

In addition to his Surgeon General responsibilities, Thompson leads the ACHI, which is jointly supported by the UAMS,

Arkansas Department of Health, and Arkansas BlueCross BlueShield. The ACHI is a nonpartisan, independent health policy center dedicated to improving the health of Arkansans. The center's work focuses on three major initiatives: healthcare financing, disease prevention and health promotion, and access to quality care. ACHI's mission is to be a catalyst for improving the health of Arkansans through evidence-based research, public issues advocacy, and collaborative program development. It does not directly provide healthcare or public health services, and it does not offer degree-granting educational programs. What the ACHI does is to stimulate, support, and complement the work of other Arkansas institutions and groups committed to health improvement. It serves as a resource for improving Arkansans' health by linking and coordinating academic personnel, health professionals, and other collaborators. The ACHI also plays a critical role in reversing the childhood obesity epidemic in Arkansas.

In 2003, the Arkansas Legislature mandated improved access to healthier foods in schools, the creation of local committees to promote physical activity and nutrition, and restrictions on student access to vending machines and on their content. More controversially, the legislation also called for annual reporting of the BMI of more than 400,000 public school students in the state to their parents. The legislation, known as Act 1220, cleared committee and both houses of the Legislature and was signed into law by Gov. Mike Huckabee in an accelerated time frame. A key reason for quick passage was that both Huckabee and Speaker of the House Herschel Cleveland faced personal health crises of their own at the time. The governor had been diagnosed with Type 2 diabetes as a result of obesity, and the speaker had just experienced a cardiac event. Faced with term limits, both recognized that improvement of the health status of a state that consistently ranked among the least healthy of all states could be their leadership legacy. The swift enactment of the legislation amazed Thompson, but as he says, "Luck is the confluence of preparation and opportunity."

Act 1220 was an unfunded mandate requiring creativity from stakeholders to accomplish its implementation. Under Thompson's leadership, the ACHI agreed to take on the challenge of implementing the BMI assessment and reporting portion of Arkansas' first-in-the-nation approach to addressing the childhood obesity epidemic.

In 2002, an Obesity Summit convened by Thompson and the ACHI had pulled together the clinical, public health, and research communities as one of the first steps in addressing the epidemic. Many of the summit's recommendations found their way into the legislative language of Act 1220.   ●   A key observation emerged from the summit: because of the amount of time children spend there, schools affect their health habits.

● A key observation emerged from the summit: because of the amount of time children spend there, schools affect their health habits.

Another recommendation — that constructive approaches to obesity must balance input from school and health officials alike — emerged from the summit. Act 1220 created a statewide Child Health Advisory Committee, which was balanced between school and health officials, and which could make direct recommendations to the Board of Education without going through the governor or the Legislature. Thompson points out that all of the facets of public health framing — evidence-based research, collaboration, and legislation — were used to address childhood obesity in a strategic way.

As a pediatrician, Thompson had always viewed prevention as being critical to his profession. He found, however, that not all pediatricians were supportive of a state-mandated effort to reduce obesity through the schools. Some pediatricians did not fully recognize the childhood obesity epidemic nor did they appreciate the potential for life-shortening diseases that could plague overweight children. In Arkansas, a good weight often meant extra layers of fat.

This lack of consensus among the state's doctors, along with limited assurance that children were even seeing their doctors on a regular basis, reinforced the strategy of assessing BMI in schools, where vision, hearing, and scoliosis were already being assessed. The next steps were to enlist the assistance of school nurses to accomplish the BMI measurement for every child and to provide training to ensure quality results.   ● Strategies to safeguard the program included many innovative approaches, including having children step on the scale backward to protect confidentiality.

Without legislative funding, another issue to be addressed was providing standardized measurement equipment to all schools, a necessity for yielding reliable data. The solution came in the form of a partnership with the Department of Corrections, where the requisite number of durable stadiometers (which measure BMI height and weight ratios) were manufactured for distribution to the state's 335 school districts at nominal costs.

The next challenge was to gain the consent of district superin-tendents. This was done by framing BMI assessment in the same context as hearing and vision screening which were already being done by schools. School principals became the key implementers of the policy and consulted with their own parent advisory committees to quell any anxiety over the new screening process.

Act 1220 further mandated that vending machines be kept off limits until 30 minutes after school lunch times, that at least half of the vending machine contents be composed of healthy foods, that cafeteria staff be trained in food preparation and nutrition, that 30 minutes of physical activity be added to every child's day, and that local committees be created to promote physical activity and nutrition. As a result, some positive changes and innovative ideas have developed. Additional physical activity has been introduced in some schools by having the school bus stop a half-mile walk from the school. In good weather, children arrive fresh from a brisk walk, not having lost one minute of instructional time during the school day. Pouring contracts at schools (usually with the Coca-Cola Co. or PepsiCo Inc., and some for shockingly high dollar figures) have been amended to include healthier

●

Strategies to safeguard the program included many innovative approaches, including having children step on the scale back-ward to protect confidentiality.

choices in the vending machines. Many school cafeterias have removed deep fryers and found healthier ways to prepare items traditionally fried. Some schools even conduct taste tests with students in an effort to develop menus that are not only healthy but that children will actually eat.

Looking back at 2003 – 2004, the first year of the project, Thompson regrets two missteps. In the original legislation, the BMI was required to be added to the student's report card. This had the potential for sending a negative or mixed message, because BMI scores are not a grade but rather one indicator of a child's overall health. Legislative modification allowed separate development of a health report to assist parental education and information. In addition, there was a small, but loud, negative public response. Thompson's name and phone number appeared on a total of 427,000 health reports that first year. Of that number, he received 300 phone calls from parents, half seeking clarification information, the remaining half with complaints. He says, ● "Taking 150 complaint calls as a result of 427,000 BMI reports is a very low percentage and better than we expected with the launch of a new program like this." Currently, the health report is mailed in confidence to parents over the principal's signature, with the potential for longitudinal data and inclusion of other health screens under consideration.

●

"Taking 150 complaint calls as a result of 427,000 BMI reports is a very low percentage and better than we expected with the launch of a new program like this."

Thompson also regrets not having the foresight to make drinking water more readily available at every school. By placing vending machines off limits until 30 minutes after lunch, a ready source of bottled water was also placed off limits at many schools that lacked drinking fountains.

In the third school year (2005 – 2006), the Body Mass Index Assessment Project began to yield results. Nearly 434,000 BMI assessments were done for children in grades K-12 throughout the state, a 99 percent participation rate, and the percentage of overweight children declined to 20.4 from 20.8 the year before. The percentage of children at risk for overweight declined to

17.1 from 17.2, and the percentage of healthy children increased to 60.6 from 60.1.   ●   While these results may not be huge, they indicate a halt of the progression of childhood obesity in Arkansas.

Paper reporting was completely eliminated during the 2006 – 2007 school year, and all data were collected electronically. By any measure, the Body Mass Index Assessment Project is a beacon for other states, but only if their legislatures act with Arkansas' speed and if they have the leadership that the ACHI and Thompson provided in Arkansas. ❀

●

While these results may not be huge, they indicate a halt of the progression of childhood obesity in Arkansas.

Lessons Learned

$\mathcal{T}$he careers of Richmond and Thompson illustrate the role of policy education and communication in changing society and, in particular, how effective social, legislative, media, and education strategies can change individual behavior and improve the overall health of populations.

Key lessons emerge from the work of these two visionary leaders.

The Role of Public Health in Policy

Richmond and Thompson demonstrate the essential link between creating policy and creating environments in which individuals and communities can choose to pursue health. Under Richmond's leadership, health promotion and prevention became the mission of the Public Health Service, and his *Healthy People* reports began to establish tangible national goals for public health.

Thompson, at the state level, has been working with Arkansas' public school system to implement a legislated policy with the goal of immediate public health benefits. His BMI screening program is an example of a local health promotion policy that can be equally effective at the national level.

Sound Policy Analysis in Public Health Practice

As Richmond points out, neither the growing knowledge base about the benefits of prevention nor political power are enough to change behavior. However, when policymakers can link an effective social strategy with an accepted health promotion policy, individual behavior change is more likely to occur. The support of policy is critical if individuals and communities are to improve their health.

For Thompson, all of the facets of framing public health such as evidence-based research, collaboration, and legislation, were used

to address childhood obesity in a strategic way. By framing BMI
assessment in the same context as hearing and vision screening
already being done by schools, he was able to convince district
administrators and school principals to become key policy
implementers.

The Role of Individuals

Richmond's leadership at the federal level pushed health promotion to the forefront of public health.   ●   He understood that
promoting health is an ongoing process and requires commitment
to behavior change, first in individuals, and then in the community.
By establishing a revision and publication cycle for the *Healthy People*
reports, he ensured that the public would be exposed to health
promotion messages on an ongoing basis.

Thompson refers to himself as a trusted broker, one who can
negotiate and bring together differing viewpoints in the service
of a common goal. His leadership presents itself in empowering
other stakeholders to implement policies and in finding ways
around obstacles that could derail the collective effort.

Advocacy for Public Health Policy

Richmond knew intuitively that the widespread media coverage
of his *Healthy People* report could spur incremental change in
individual behavior. Similarly, Thompson knew that his state
could move forward with an innovative childhood obesity project
only if all sectors in Arkansas — policymakers, school administrators, health officials, parents, and commercial interests —
were in accord.

Both stories demonstrate that when leaders advocate for evidence-
based health promotion and when policymakers implement
it effectively, the impact on improving the health of an entire
population can be tangible and visible in the short term.
Richmond's and Thompson's advocacy efforts were sensitive

●

He understood
that promoting
health is an
ongoing process
and requires
commitment to
behavior change,
first in individuals,
and then in the
community.

to the complex multidisciplinary nature of promoting health through education, environmental change, behavior change, and health system reform.

● Both of these public health leaders know that joining knowledge and political power will lead to great accomplishments in the long run. What is essential is faith in the continued growth of the knowledge base, the inevitability of political will that responds to overwhelming evidence, and shrewd social strategies that can bring the two together. ❁ ❁

● Both of these public health leaders know that joining knowledge and political power will lead to great accomplishments in the long run.

References

1. Simmons-Morton B, Greene WH, Gottlieb NH. Introduction to health education and health promotion. 2nd ed. Long Grove: Waveland Press; 1995.
2. Simmons-Morton B, Greene WH, Gottlieb NH 95.
3. Simmons-Morton B, Greene WH, Gottlieb NH 95.
4. World Health Organization Regional Office for Europe [Home page on the Internet]. Denmark. Ottawa Charter for Health Promotion, 1986. [updated 2006 Aug 1; cited 2007 April 18]. Available from: http://www.euro.who.int/AboutWHO/Policy/20010827_2.
5. United States Department of Health and Human Services – Office of the Surgeon General [Home page on the Internet]. Washington, DC: About the Office of the Surgeon General. [updated 2007 June 14; cited 2007 April 18]. Available from: http://www.surgeongeneral.gov/aboutoffice.html.
6. United States Department of Health and Human Services – Office of the Surgeon General [Home page on the Internet]. Washington, DC: History of the Office of the Surgeon General. [updated 2007 Jan 4; cited 2007 April 18]. Available from: http://www.surgeongeneral.gov/sghist.htm.
7. United States Department of Health and Human Services – Office of the Surgeon General [Home page on the Internet]. Washington, DC: Luther Leonidas Terry (1961-1965). [updated 2007 Jan 4; cited 2007 April 18]. Available from: http://www.surgeongeneral.gov/library/history/bioterry.htm.
8. United States Department of Health and Human Services – Office of the Surgeon General [Home page on the Internet]. Washington, DC: Julius B. Richmond (1977-1981). [updated 2007 Jan 4; cited 2007 April 18]. Available from: http://www.surgeongeneral.gov/library/history/biorichmond.htm.
9. Simmons-Morton B, Greene WH, Gottlieb NH 93.
10. United States Department of Health and Human Services – Office of the Surgeon General [Home page on the Internet]. Washington, DC: Julius B. Richmond (1977-1981). [updated 2007 Jan 4; cited 2007 April 18]. Available from: http://www.surgeongeneral.gov/library/history/biorichmond.htm.
11. United States Department of Health and Human Services – Office of the Surgeon General [Home page on the Internet]. Washington, DC: Julius B. Richmond (1977-1981). [updated 2007 Jan 4; cited 2007 April 18]. Available from: http://www.surgeongeneral.gov/library/history/biorichmond.htm.
12. United States Department of Health and Human Services – Office of the Surgeon General [Home page on the Internet]. Washington, DC: David Satcher (1998-2002). [updated 2007 Jan 4; cited 2007 April 18]. Available from: http://www.surgeongeneral.gov/library/history/biosatcher.htm.
13. United States Department of Health and Human Services [Home page on the Internet]. Washington, DC: *Healthy People 2010.* [cited 2007 April 18]. Available from: http://www.healthypeople.gov/Publications/.
14. Kreuter MW; Directors of Health Promotion and Education. State health promotion capacity: a DHPE assessment report. July 2003. [cited 2007 April 18]. Available from: http://www.dhpe.org/StateHealthPromotionCapacityReport.doc.

Chapter 7.   **Walking the Talk:**
             Proving the Case for Prevention

Introduction

$\mathcal{A}$n ounce of prevention is worth a pound of cure. This
well-known saying should be the foundation of every healthcare
system. However, many systems, including that of the United
States, have traditionally focused their resources on the cure,
not the prevention. Over the last few decades, the public health
community has been increasingly effective in shifting this focus
by demonstrating the benefits of prevention from an economic
and health perspective.

●

Prevention refers
to interventions
by individuals,
society, and the
healthcare system
to avoid threats
to individual and
population health
from disease, the
environment, or
other causes.

●   Prevention refers to interventions by individuals, society,
and the healthcare system to avoid threats to individual and
population health from disease, the environment, or other causes.
Primary prevention involves preventing illness, disease, or injury from
occurring in the first place; an example might be abstinence
or safe-sex practices to avoid the HIV virus. *Secondary prevention*
involves detecting and preventing the progression of conditions
before they become symptomatic; in this case, a person diagnosed
with HIV but exhibiting no symptoms might begin antiretroviral
therapy and continue using safe practices to prevent transmission
of the virus to others. *Tertiary prevention* involves preventing the
progression and complications of conditions in which symptoms
are already occurring. Here, the individual may have full-blown
AIDS and would be on a regimen of drug therapies and other
interventions to manage the disease.

A considerable body of research proves that practicing prevention
in the clinical setting can prevent and, in some cases, foster
the early detection of disease. In turn, this leads to prevention
of secondary and tertiary consequences and premature death.

Examples of clinical preventive services are screening tests with high predictive value in the early detection of disease, such as mammograms, and vaccine administration to prevent the occurrence of disease. Counseling by health professionals also can lead to behavioral changes that reduce the rate and severity of disease.[1]

● Evidence-based guidelines for preventive services are a recent hallmark of public health policy. Many professional organizations develop guidelines for various conditions but since the mid-1980s one group of experts, the U.S. Preventive Services Task Force (USPSTF), has used rigorous, formal criteria to assess all relevant studies and to offer evidence-based recommendations for the full range of clinical preventive services. The expert members of the USPSTF are not from federal agencies and, therefore, offer independent views. The relevant federal agencies do provide support to the Task Force, however, to ensure a thorough review. The work of the Task Force has been formally issued as the comprehensive *Guide to Clinical Preventive Services*, published in 1989, 1996, and 2005. The guide firmly established the proof of effectiveness of clinical preventive services and set the stage for progress in evidence-based medical treatment as well.

●

Evidence-based guidelines for preventive services are a recent hallmark of public health policy.

An example of the guide's impact is the role it served in enhancing Medicare. Experts in the health status and healthcare needs of Medicare beneficiaries have posited that clinical preventive services and population-based interventions can improve the health of older adults significantly.[2] Understanding the importance of preventive services for the older population has grown in recent years as a result of mounting evidence regarding their value, as well as improved technologies for the delivery of preventive treatments for conditions such as high blood pressure and elevated cholesterol.[3] However, with the exception of certain specified clinical screening assessments and immunizations for selected health risks,[4] Medicare traditionally has emphasized coverage of acute and post-acute treatment and has excluded coverage of routine physical assessments. In fact, the original statute expressly prohibited preventive services. Medicare's traditional orientation as a payer of acute and post-acute care means that Medicare beneficiaries receive recommended clinical preventive services at a relatively low rate.[5]

In 2003 Congress enacted legislation as part of the Medicare Prescription Drug, Improvement and Modernization Act (MMA) that broadened Medicare coverage of clinical preventive services. An initial preventive physical examination is available within the first six months of Part B enrollment for beneficiaries who gained Part B coverage on or after Jan. 1, 2005. The amendments also broaden covered screening assessments to include cardiovascular disease and diabetes.[6] These new benefits are expected to further reorient Medicare coverage toward prevention in keeping with evidence of the effectiveness of clinical preventive services.

Although Medicare is the most prominent example, most forms of insurance offer only limited coverage of evidence-based clinical preventive services.[7] More recently, insurers have begun to improve coverage of certain recommended preventive services, such as breast cancer screening, cervical cancer screening, and immunizations,[8] and have developed performance measures and payment incentives to encourage their use.[9]   ●   Nonetheless, even as some 47 million Americans remain uninsured, millions more are underinsured when it comes to clinical preventive services. Improving and strengthening health insurance coverage so that recommended clinical preventive services are accessible to all is a consummate example of public health policy leadership.

> ●
>
> Nonetheless, even as some 47 million Americans remain uninsured, millions more are underinsured when it comes to clinical preventive services.

The national case study that follows examines the contributions of J. Michael McGinnis, MD, MPP, and Steven H. Woolf, MD, to the U.S. Preventive Services Task Force, now in its third decade. The Task Force reviews the medical literature and publishes evidence-based guidelines for preventive services that guide policymakers in their decisions and assist clinicians with the advice they give patients. From its beginnings with a staff of one in the Office of the Deputy Assistant Secretary for Health during the

Reagan administration, the U.S. Preventive Services Task Force has grown to occupy several hallways within the Agency for Healthcare Research and Quality (AHRQ), its institutional home since 1995. The Task Force, reconstituted with appropriate expertise as needed for new issues and editions, continually publishes updates on evidence-based preventive services as they become available.

The local case study examines prevention at the clinical level through the delivery of prenatal care. It chronicles how the leadership of one public health pioneer, Godfrey Oakley, MD, MSPM, galvanized the fight against birth defects by advocating for a simple pre-pregnancy intervention. Once again, the evidence for prevention was used to change policy at the national level. As expected, policy change came slowly and was not without controversy. ✿

National Case Study

J. Michael McGinnis, Steven H. Woolf, and the U.S. Preventive Services Task Force

J. Michael McGinnis, MD, MPP

Steven H. Woolf, MD

The U.S. Preventive Services Task Force was established in 1983 and was modeled after the Canadian Task Force on the Periodic Health Examination. Convened in 1976 by Walter Spitzer, an epidemiologist at McGill University, that Task Force published the results of its literature review of certain selected preventive services in the *Canadian Medical Journal* in 1979. The rigorous methodology developed by the Canadian Task Force, giving the greatest weight to randomized control trials (considered the gold standard for clinical research), served as the basis for the U.S. Task Force's approach to its evidence review of preventive services. When J. Michael McGinnis, MD, MPP, deputy surgeon general and deputy assistant secretary for health, established the U.S. Task Force in 1983, prevention and evidence-based medicine were new concepts being addressed together for the first time at the national level.

McGinnis is that rare political appointee in the federal government whose service spanned both Democratic and Republican administrations. He joined the Department of Health, Education and Welfare (HEW, now the Department of Health and Human Services, or HHS) in 1977 in the early days of the Carter administration and departed government service in 1995 during the Clinton administration. During those 18 years, he was responsible for disease prevention policies and for coordinating work at the federal level on disease prevention and health promotion. In between, he created the U.S. Preventive Services Task Force under President Ronald Reagan's first HHS secretary, Richard Schweiker, a former Republican governor and U.S. senator from Pennsylvania.

Born in Columbia, Mo., and raised in California, McGinnis majored in political theory as an undergraduate at the University of California at Berkeley after having completed all the prerequisites for medical school. There, professor Ray Sontag, an expert on European diplomatic history, inspired him and deepened his appreciation of the larger political sphere in which things play out. Interested in international health, he attended medical school at the University of California at Los Angeles because it was the only medical school that would allow him to earn a master's degree in political science (with an emphasis in international relations) at the same time. After graduating from medical school and completing his residency at a time when the military draft was still in effect, McGinnis completed his military service by working in the International Division of the HEW secretary's office. He served as a medical diplomat overseeing the U.S. health exchange programs with Eastern Europe. During this time, he was recruited by D.A. Henderson, the head of the World Health Organization's Smallpox Eradication Program, for a three-month assignment as a field epidemiologist in India — an assignment that turned into a year when he was asked to oversee the work in Uttar Pradesh, India's largest state, until its conclusion.

Although McGinnis never earned a Master of Public Health degree, his commitment to public health was clear from the beginning and the work in India started him on an inescapable path. He returned to the United States with an interest in obtaining more training in policy analysis, and he earned a master's degree in public policy at Harvard University's Kennedy School of Government. That decision proved to be a very important step in his career path. It was at the Kennedy School that his mentor, Richard Neustadt, responding to a request from Joseph Califano, Jr., President Carter's newly appointed secretary of HEW, recommended that McGinnis join the new administration. Late in the winter of 1977 and even before completing his degree, McGinnis began his Washington career in health policy, initially as a special assistant to the secretary and then deputy assistant secretary for health and director of disease prevention and health promotion policy.

The USPSTF grew out of McGinnis' deeply held belief that
progress in the delivery of preventive services would require
a comprehensive and incontrovertible marshaling of the evidence.
Established in 1983, the work of the USPSTF actually began in
1984 with a staff of one — Angela Mickalide, as Task Force
coordinator. Initially, she and McGinnis relied on Task Force
members for most of the review work, which was coordinated and
supported by a family physician, Dr. Robert Fried, who had joined
McGinnis' staff for a two-year assignment as a Luther Terry
Fellow. The work was supplemented by residents in preventive
medicine from Johns Hopkins University, who rotated through
the office as part of a "real-world practicum." Steven Woolf, MD,
was one of those residents. In 1987, he joined the staff of the
USPSTF on a full-time basis and reported to Dr. Douglas
Kamerow, who was to remain with the USPSTF in a leadership
role through its transition to AHRQ in 1995 and beyond.

Woolf's role was to manage the literature review and to strengthen
the systematic application of the methodology for judging the
evidence. He took immediately to the work and the mission of
the Task Force, lending his expertise, vision, commitment, and
experience as both a full-time staff member from 1987 to 1995
and then as a Task Force member from 1998 to 2003. He was
also a senior advisor to the Task Force through AHRQ from
2004 to 2007. Today, he focuses his academic work at Virginia
Commonwealth University on improving the quality of preventive
services delivery in primary care settings. Woolf is also involved
with social justice issues, including the adverse health influences
of poverty and racial and ethnic disparities.

At first, McGinnis suggested that the assessment for each topic
should take up no more than one page in the published document.
In contrast, Woolf believed that the body of the evidence required
more thorough reporting in the publication. Ultimately, the Task
Force agreed that recommendations could range from as little as
one page to as many as several hundred pages, depending upon the
evidence. Woolf explains the Task Force process as breaking down

the question into pieces and looking at the analytic logic behind doing something clinically. With regard to screening for prostate cancer, for example, what is the rationale for the screening test and does it find the condition accurately? If it finds the condition, how effectively does early detection improve health outcomes, and do the benefits of doing so outweigh the harm? Once the pieces of the puzzle are assembled, a second and critical part of the process applies a system for grading the quality of the evidence for each piece. After the Task Force applies rigorous methodologies to the evidence, a possible outcome is that a widely prescribed preventive service will no longer be recommended because of insufficient evidence.

The origins of the Task Force date to the late 1970s with the publication, under McGinnis' direction, of the first Surgeon General's report on health promotion and disease prevention, known as *Healthy People*. ● This report set out a conceptual framework for prevention and established broad health improvement goals for the nation to target with its prevention activities. The idea of *Healthy People* had grown out of his experience on the Ganges Plain in India, where the smallpox eradication program succeeded because it set measurable targets for smallpox reduction by geographic area and tracked the progress monthly, adjusting resource allocation accordingly until the disease was eradicated. In his policy role in the Carter administration, McGinnis asked why targets could not be set and tracked in key areas of importance to the overall health of the U.S. population. The result was the publication of *Healthy People* in 1979 with targets to be achieved by 1990. The *Healthy People* process continues today with work under way to establish targets for the year 2020. Because several of the *Healthy People* goals were dependent on progress in the delivery of clinical preventive services, McGinnis then turned his attention to employers and insurers, seeking to involve them more constructively in the health of workers. The benefits that employers provide in their insurance packages for employees were a key element in this effort.

●

[*Healthy People*] set out a conceptual framework for prevention and established broad health improvement goals for the nation to target with its prevention activities.

Here he encountered substantial resistance. McGinnis found that both employers and insurers were consistently asking, "Where's the proof?" This was in part a reflection of their focus on bottom line issues and in part a dodge to avoid paying for the services. Employers and insurers did not inherently oppose covering screenings and immunizations, but they needed to know that the costs for these services were warranted and that they would, in fact, improve the health of workers. With the Canadian study just published in 1979 and with the exhaustive research studies that had been conducted over the preceding 20 years now part of the medical literature, McGinnis viewed the science base for preventive services as possibly more advanced than that for the full range of clinical treatment services. Extensive evidence had been compiled for treating high blood pressure and cholesterol and for using immunizations to forestall epidemics, among other preventive services. Rather than review and report each service individually in separate activities, McGinnis thought the best approach would be a U.S. effort that was comprehensive and used rigorous and consistent analytic approaches, similar to the Canadian Task Force. This led to a decision to publish guidelines on all services at once, rather than on a piecemeal basis.

The first step was to charter the Task Force as independent of the federal government so that members would not be constrained by agency or political factors. McGinnis arranged for supplemental funding from the Kellogg Foundation, then led by Tom Bruce, to gain private sector support in addition to federal monies. As an entity outside government, ● the Task Force would have not only the implicit stamp of government authority, because the government nurtured it along the way, but also the scientific integrity of an independent enterprise.

The Task Force would have not only the implicit stamp of government authority... but also the scientific integrity of an independent enterprise.

The next step was to appoint a group of Task Force members who represented a wide variety of disciplines and expertise from around the country. A number of primary care physicians joined, including Paul Frame, a family doctor who had previously published a series of monographs addressing the need for guidelines on preventive services. Robert Lawrence, a professor at that time at Harvard University School of Medicine and now at Johns Hopkins University, agreed to chair the Task Force. (Lawrence later became an important mentor for Woolf through his wide-ranging travels on behalf of human rights.) The Task Force, numbering approximately 20, included dentists, health economists, nurses, and social scientists. At the first meeting in Bethesda in 1984, Walter Spitzer was invited to review the work of the Canadian group as a key reference point for the work of the U.S. Task Force.   ●   After four years examining evidence found throughout the medical literature, the Task Force published its findings in 1989 as *The Guide to Clinical Preventive Services*.

The Task Force faced challenges during those four years of exhaustive work. Chief among them was that large organizations were, in effect, interest groups for the various diseases and conditions with which the Task Force was dealing. As experts in the field, these organizations, including the federal government's National Institutes of Health (NIH), had previously issued reasonable recommendations offering their best judgment. The American Cancer Society, for example, made recommendations on mammography and colon cancer screening, but these were grounded more in their expertise than in rigorous, specific rules of evidence. The Task Force often found itself in conflict with some of the largest interest groups, with differences on how to interpret the science nearly always the cause. To overcome resistance, the Task Force shared preliminary guidelines with the various interest groups along the way. The guidelines often aroused controversy when one group or another thought the rules of evidence used by the Task Force were too restrictive for their circumstances. The only direct political conflict, before the publication of the first report in 1989, involved the guide's discussion on counseling related to family planning and abortion, but the status of the Task Force as a nongovernmental entity protected those guidelines from interference.

Another challenge for the Task Force was that clinicians pride themselves on their autonomy. The guidelines could be viewed

●

After four years examining evidence found throughout the medical literature, the Task Force published its findings in 1989 as *The Guide to Clinical Preventive Services.*

as stifling their independent culture, which made it even more imperative that the evidence for recommending certain preventive services be weighed so carefully that clinicians would accept the recommendations. Yet another challenge was a decision by McGinnis to rule out cost as a factor in the Task Force's review of the scientific evidence. Because the intent of this initial effort was to marshal the full weight of the science, he wanted their findings to be based purely on health merits. ● In this respect, if the Task Force recommended something *not* be done, that decision would be based entirely on health outcomes, not cost. McGinnis, of course, realized that cost represented an important issue. He later established a parallel effort to address that dimension: the Panel on Cost Effectiveness in Medicine and Health.

●

In this respect, if the Task Force recommended something *not* be done, that decision would be based entirely on health outcomes, not cost.

The full engagement of the Task Force members throughout the four years far exceeded McGinnis' optimistic hopes. He had expected a strong commitment but the team threw itself into every task with unfailing dedication. Faced with skepticism from professional societies, McGinnis established a parallel group called the National Coordinating Committee on Clinical Preventive Services. The membership consisted not of individual members but of professional organizations, such as the American Medical Association, the American College of Obstetrics and Gynecology, the American Academy of Pediatrics, and the American Academy of Family Physicians. The Task Force kept the coordinating committee informed about progress, and when the guidelines were finally issued, there was a strong familiarity and almost a marriage between the leadership of the professional organizations and the work of the Task Force. McGinnis says, "There could be a handing off of the baton — here's what the science says, this is what you need to implement." After sparking many initial controversies, this direct collaboration on the evidence base made smoother hand-offs possible.

McGinnis says, "The enterprise had a much larger impact than we even expected. We expected to provide a resource that would be very useful to clinicians and insurers, effect changes in the terms of the debate around reimbursement for clinical preventive services, and set in motion something that might have a longer life. All of these things happened, but in addition, the work of the Task Force set the stage for the entire national focus on evidence-based medicine." He adds, "We were transparent about the rules for using the science base, reviewing all the science in each specific area and basing our recommendations solely on the evidence. From that point, it has grown and is universally viewed as the model for evidence-based medicine."

In its new home at AHRQ, the U.S. Preventive Services Task Force has a large, formal institutional base that is not subjected to the political process. McGinnis was happy to see the AHRQ transfer occur as he left government in 1995, and was pleased that Kamerow continued to oversee the work of the Task Force in its new home. During his years at HHS, McGinnis also advanced other public health policies, founding the Nutrition Policy Board that developed dietary guidelines and launching the Interagency Committee on Human Nutrition and Research, a joint activity between HHS and the Department of Agriculture. After several years in philanthropy with the Robert Wood Johnson Foundation, he now works with the Institute of Medicine at the National Academy of Sciences overseeing initiatives in evidence-based medicine, taking the lessons of the Task Force beyond the field of prevention into the arena of medical care for the whole nation. McGinnis says, ● "The notion of evidence-based medicine is essentially the principle of first ensuring that science drives policy and, secondly, that policy yields the best allocation of resources. Basically, that's public health." For him, "It's the most exciting field you can imagine, because it's a blend of science and politics and has the ability to affect people in the most fundamentally positive ways."

"The notion of evidence-based medicine is essentially the principle of first ensuring that science drives policy and, secondly, that policy yields the best allocation of resources. Basically, that's public health." ●

The experience of Godfrey Oakley, MD, MSPM, at the Centers for Disease Control and Prevention (CDC) illustrates that blending science and politics to change clinical obstetric practice can prevent a significant congenital disease.

Local Case Study

Godfrey Oakley and the Fight to Prevent Spina Bifida With Folic Acid

*Godfrey Oakley,
MD, MSPM*

Spina bifida is a birth defect involving incomplete development of the neural tube in the fetus. It can be compared with a zipper that starts in the middle and proceeds in two directions.[10] Spina bifida results if the zipper at the bottom end of the neural tube, where the spinal cord meets the brain, is incomplete. Depending on the completeness of the zippering process, it almost always results in some degree of paralysis and problems with bladder and bowel control. Anencephaly results if the zipper at the top end is incomplete, leaving the brain exposed. Anencephaly is almost always fatal either in uterus or shortly after birth.

When Godfrey Oakley, MD, MSPM, joined the CDC in 1968, the cause for these defects was unknown. In the summer of 1991, however, the definitive study showing that folic acid could prevent spina bifida and anencephaly was published in the *Lancet*. On Sept. 11, 1992, the CDC published the Public Health Service (PHS) recommendation stating that every woman of reproductive age capable of becoming pregnant consume 400 micrograms of folic acid daily.[11,12] It was not until 1996 that Oakley and his team at the CDC succeeded in getting the FDA to require that flour millers add 140 micrograms of folic acid to each 100 grams of enriched flour — a concentration that would result in the average woman consuming 100 micrograms of folic acid a day.[13] A randomized control trial conducted by the CDC in China affirmed that the PHS recommendation was valid.[14]

Raised by a single mother who was a social worker, Oakley grew up in North Carolina and attended Duke University. He earned his medical degree at Bowman Gray School of Medicine, now part of Wake Forest University, and trained in pediatrics in Cleveland during the Vietnam War. Seeking a draft deferment, he signed on as an Epidemic Intelligence Service (EIS) officer and has stayed with the CDC as an epidemiologist throughout his career. Although he has retired from government service, he still collaborates on CDC studies from his new position at the Rollins School of Public Health at Emory University in Atlanta. At the end of Oakley's two-year EIS assignment, part of which he spent in Nigeria helping William Foege with the smallpox eradication program, the CDC supported him for two years of academic training. He chose a laboratory fellowship at the University of Washington in Seattle. With a strong interest in epidemiology already engrained from his EIS work, he wandered into the brand-new School of Public Health and decided to broaden his experience beyond the lab by also earning a Master of Science in Preventive Medicine (MSPM) degree in epidemiology.

Returning to a full-time position at the CDC in the birth defects division, Oakley became fascinated with the epidemiology of spina bifida.   ●   During the 1930s, there was a great epidemic in Great Britain and the United States that was not recognized at the time. It varied by class, time, place, and person — the classic signposts for epidemiologists. It primarily affected people living in poverty, except that African-Americans living in poverty seemed to have a lessened risk as a result of genetic protection. The rates in most parts of the world were between one and two per 1,000, but in Ireland, they were five per 1,000. During the 1930s in Great Britain and the U.S., the figures rose to five per 1,000 as well. Oakley points out that when the World Health Organization (WHO) decided to eradicate polio, the 350,000 cases of polio in the world at that time matched an equivalent number of annual cases of spina bifida and anencephaly.

●

During the 1930s, there was a great epidemic in Great Britain and the United States that was not recognized at the time.

Oakley says, "Being in a research position was great because we were motivated by really smart people around us to try to find the right answer, with birth defects prevention as the underlying principle. When I was first at the CDC, I learned enough about epidemiology to see that it made nice contributions to cancer and heart disease but had not been applied to birth defects, and that was the place I thought we might be able to make some difference." He observes a truism about prevention, which is that "how" to prevent a condition is often known before the "why" is understood. ● He believes that the first message for the public should be that birth defects are preventable, as the public often believes that they are acts of God or something unavoidable in nature. Thanks to his detective work on birth defects, vitamins became an ally in preventing the devastating defects.

● [Oakley] believes that the first message for the public should be that birth defects are preventable, as the general public often believes that they are acts of God or something unavoidable in nature.

Vitamins and their link to prenatal health were discovered in the 1930s and 1940s. Between 1931 and 1933 in India, Dr. Lucy Wills studied women who died from anemia during pregnancy. Naming the condition pernicious anemia of pregnancy, she discovered that it resulted from Hindu women not eating enough folic acid. When Wills fed yeast extract to women with anemia, they got better. As it turned out, the ingredient in yeast extract that prevented the anemia was folic acid.

In 1941, natural folic acid was extracted for the first time from four tons of spinach. While folic acid is known as vitamin B-9, it needs vitamin B-12 to be metabolized and the two are, therefore, inextricably linked. Take vitamin B-12 away and cells stop dividing. Oakley says, "If you're a young embryo, essentially a factory of cells that are running at more than full speed, you start with one cell and make a gazillion cells to create a baby. We know that most people in the world have marginal levels of folic acid. If women with marginal folate status get pregnant, they are unable to make enough DNA to make the necessary cells for the baby's brain and spinal cord to develop normally."

Oakley recounts that until the early 1930s, all birth defects were thought to be genetic. The scientific community believed that the mammalian placenta could protect the fetus from any environmental harm. However, a Texas veterinarian, Dr. F. Hale, published a paper in 1937 that demonstrated that if he removed vitamin A from the diet of female pigs, they delivered piglets without eyes. Because this veterinarian at Texas A&M University experimented with nutrition as a way to boost growth in piglets, he discovered by chance that environmental factors do cause great harm to a fetus. Oakley says, ● "To me this is a great story, for it is a reminder that a dedicated person working anywhere in the world can conduct world class science." In 1941, an Australian ophthalmologist saw 10 children with cataracts and connected the condition to maternal rubella infection, thereby establishing the congenital rubella syndrome. As it turned out, rubella became preventable through the introduction of a vaccine, essentially emptying out the institutes for the blind and deaf that had proliferated throughout the world.

Meanwhile, technical advances in the treatment of spina bifida began to make it possible for children born with it to live longer lives. Once polio was eliminated in the United States in the 1950s thanks to the Salk vaccine, spina bifida became the chief cause of paralysis in infants. John Holter, a hydraulics technician in Philadelphia, faced with his own son having been born with hydrocephalus (also known as water on the brain), invented the Holter Valve to drain fluid from the brain. In the mid-1960s, professor Richard Smithells of Leeds University in England, a pediatrician interested in birth defects, collaborated with an obstetrician in Liverpool, named Bryan Hibbard, who was interested in the idea that folic acid deficiency caused placenta previa (the placenta implanted directly over the cervix). Smithells knew that spina bifida and anencephaly affected poor women more often than rich women, and taking their cue from Wills in India, they wondered if the higher rate was related to diet. Their work evolved in the 1970s to address the issue of spina bifida and anencephaly in the population, with findings that suggested, but did not prove, that a supplement of multivitamins with 360 micrograms of folic acid taken daily by women just before and in the early stages of pregnancy prevents 87 percent of spina bifida and anencephaly.[15] Because the Smithells study was not a randomized control trial, however, the findings were not embraced by the medical community.

● "To me this is a great story, for it is a reminder that a dedicated person working anywhere in the world can conduct world class science."

In the 1980s, Oakley devoted much effort at the CDC to obtain funding to conduct a randomized control trial in the United States. While NIH had just one center devoted to cancer, the work on birth defects was spread among five centers. He found it impossible to get money to study folic acid and spina bifida from either NIH or the March of Dimes. However, with Vietnam War veterans raising the issue of whether Agent Orange caused birth defects, money was available to study that phenomenon. Although they could not conduct a randomized control trial, Oakley's colleagues, including Joe Mulinare and David Erickson, used the available funding. They discovered that the rate of spina bifida was reduced by 50 percent when women expecting a child fathered by a Vietnam veteran took a multivitamin every day.[16] Despite this evidence, the lack of a randomized control trial still cast doubt on the findings.

Finally, in the late 1980s, British researcher Nick Wald succeeded in getting money from the Medical Research Council (MRC) in the U.K. to conduct a randomized control trial on folic acid and spina bifida. At 5 p.m. on June 24, 1991, while he was attending a birth defects conference in Florida, Oakley received a call from Wald that changed his life. Wald told him that the MRC vitamin study had closed because of the overwhelming evidence that folic acid prevented spina bifida. ● The study found that women who consumed 4,000 micrograms of folic acid before and during the early weeks of pregnancy had a 72 percent lower rate of spina bifida and anencephaly. Therefore, the randomized control trial would be discontinued and a recommendation that women of reproductive age take folic acid would be issued. Having been a skeptic about food as a reason for spina bifida, that phone call converted Oakley immediately.[17]

●

The study found that women who consumed 4,000 micrograms of folic acid before and during the early weeks of pregnancy had a 72 percent lower rate of spina bifida and anencephaly.

The controversy that consumed Oakley and his colleagues for the next five years was how best to deliver the folic acid recommended daily allowance (RDA) to women of reproductive age who were capable of becoming pregnant. The optimum approach for reaching the entire population at risk was to fortify flour with synthetic folic acid to meet the minimum RDA, and thereby leave

no woman uncovered who could possibly become pregnant.
However, nutrition experts at the FDA resisted enriching flour
with synthetic folic acid, and suggested that the RDA be met,
instead, through natural foods in women's daily diets. Although
Oakley pointed out that extracting enough natural folic acid from
spinach was simply impractical, nutrition experts convened by the
FDA dug in their heels. Not until the March of Dimes threatened
to fill the FDA commissioner's office with children in wheelchairs
with spina bifida did progress finally come. The March of Dimes
proved to be a critical supporter, as did members of Congress
who had been affected by birth defects within their own families.
Oakley moved the FDA panel by arranging for three adults with
spina bifida to tell heart-wrenching personal stories. ● He had
learned from his mentor William Foege that people in public
health need to put a face on the numbers.

By the beginning of 1998, every manufacturer was required
to fortify flour with enough folic acid that the average woman
would consume 100 micrograms of folic acid a day. Fortified
flour reduced the incidence of spina bifida and anencephaly and,
as an unintended consequence, helped decrease deaths from heart
attacks and strokes. It turns out that folic acid lowers homocys-
teine, heightened levels of which are associated with heart attacks
and strokes.[18,19] Pleased that he helped prevent birth defects with
folic acid, Oakley says, "If you get the data right, you can get
the policy right."

The work continued, however, with an outbreak of anencephaly
in the Brownsville area of southern Texas in the late 1990s.
This outbreak was used as an example by environmental activists
to embargo goods from Mexico that were not manufactured up
to U.S. standards. But Oakley and collaborators from the March
of Dimes saw this as an opportunity for a careful epidemiological
investigation. Without funding from the March of Dimes, the
investigation would have floundered. In 1999, the Brownsville
outbreak became the impetus for establishing the National Center
on Birth Defects and Developmental Disabilities at the CDC. ❋

●

[Oakley] had
learned from his
mentor William
Foege that
people in public
health need to
put a face on the
numbers.

Lessons Learned

*P*revention is the cornerstone to ensuring a healthy population, but public health policy has lagged in shifting the focus of clinical care toward prevention. Thanks to the work of McGinnis, Woolf, and Oakley, prevention has been winning more battles to earn its rightful place in the healthcare landscape. Their case studies reveal important lessons on how using evidence-based guidelines can change policy for not only clinical care but for the prevention of disease as well.

The Role of Public Health in Policy

Prevention has grown to become a key contributor to the overall health of the U.S. population, but it still pales in comparison to resources used to find cures and mechanisms of disease. McGinnis, Woolf, and Oakley would concur that a greater share of healthcare dollars used for prevention is needed and would help strike a more even and necessary balance with that for research into mechanisms of disease and their cures. ● They would also concur that epidemiology, a field that promotes prevention and plays a key role in public health, should be among the most esteemed specialties within healthcare. While epidemiology may lead to cures, its day-to-day work promotes prevention, protecting the population from disease outbreaks, environmental hazards, and risk factors that result from behavior and lifestyle choices.

●
They would also concur that epidemiology, a field that promotes prevention and plays a key role in public health, should be among the most esteemed specialties within healthcare.

Oakley's ultimate success in winning approval from the FDA to enrich flour with folic acid illustrates how guidelines for preventive services have established beachheads in clinical care. The guidelines may be as simple and sensible as recommending a childhood vaccine, or they may be complex, as the example of folic acid illustrates. Regardless of how the guidelines are developed, once providers accept them, insurers are more likely to follow. Once insurers cover a preventive service broadly, they help pave the way for it to become an accepted practice in clinical care. In this manner, public health policy achieves its mission of strengthening the focus on population health through preventive services.

Sound Policy Analysis in Public Health Practice

The U.S. Preventive Services Task Force helped to alter the unfavorable balance between prevention and treatment within healthcare. After assembling a group of dedicated, highly respected professionals representing primary care in all its facets, the Task Force marshaled the available evidence and made recommendations on preventive services that would assist clinicians in advising their patients. ● The methodologies had to be unassailable for controversies to be surmounted, and the Task Force's work quickly became an invaluable resource for clinicians. Thanks to the tentative first steps with evidence-based medicine spearheaded by McGinnis and Woolf, along with members of the Task Force, an entirely new movement for evidence-based medicine has matured in the United States.

Oakley knew that he would need a strong evidence base to convince the FDA to take a stand on folic acid. Randomized control trials, the gold standard of medicine, are difficult to fund and often delay advances in science and, therefore, lead to delays in policy. This is especially true for advances in prevention. Oakley was grateful for the work of other researchers, such as Nick Wald, who were able to provide the evidence of the benefits of folic acid before his own clinical trial was under way.

The Role of Individuals

Woolf defines leadership as a combination of clarity of principles and management style. He says, "You need to know where you want to go, but you also need the right qualities to bring people along with you." For McGinnis, he views his career as having been built around one fundamental mandate: changing the terms of the debate; that is, making sure that issues were framed in a fashion that allowed the right things to happen.

● The methodologies had to be unassailable for controversies to be surmounted, and the Task Force's work quickly became an invaluable resource for clinicians.

Oakley has devoted his professional life to the field of epidemiology. Yet he applied his skills and experience broadly, even taking on a federal agency in a multiyear battle to change federal requirements for folic acid supplementation. In helping to change health policy by focusing on prevention, Oakley changed the course of countless lives. Because of his efforts, along with those of the March of Dimes and other committed individuals, fewer and fewer babies are born with spina bifida.

Advocacy for Public Health Policy

McGinnis and his colleagues knew that the medical community would not embrace being told how to practice acute or preventive medicine. To avert these controversies, the Task Force collaborated with medical societies throughout the guidelines development process, earning their trust and a place for evidence-based medicine within healthcare. Interest groups, whether large federal agencies such as the FDA or professional medical societies, are stakeholders in the process of improving prevention through evidence-based medicine. ● When they resist advances because of their own interests, a solid base of evidence is the best way to convert them into advocates.

> ●
> When [stakeholders] resist advances because of their own interests, a solid base of evidence is the best way to convert them into advocates.

Similarly, it was not until the March of Dimes began to advocate for a folic acid policy that progress was finally made. The March of Dimes proved to be a critical supporter of Oakley's efforts. In addition, Oakley let individuals born with spina bifida speak for themselves. Their testimonies had a dramatic effect on moving the new policy forward. Oakley remembered the lesson of his mentor, William Foege, who taught him that people in public health need to put a face on the numbers. ❊ ❊

References

1. Partnership for Prevention [Home page on the Internet].Washington, DC: Executive summary: a better Medicare for healthier seniors: recommendations to modernize Medicare's prevention policies 2003. [cited 2007 Aug 27]. Available from: http://www.prevent.org/images/stories/Files/publications/medicare.pdf.

2. Partnership for Prevention [Home page on the Internet]. Washington, DC: Preventive care: a national profile on use, disparities, and health benefits. 2007. [cited 2007 Aug 27]. Available from: http://www.prevent.org/images/stories/2007/ncpp/ncpp%20preventive%20care%20report.pdf.

3. Partnership for Prevention [Home page on Internet].Washington, DC: Executive summary: a better medicare for healthier seniors: recommendations to modernize medicare's prevention policies 2003. [cited 2007 Aug 27]. Available from: http://www.prevent.org/images/stories/Files/publications/medicare.pdf.

4. Institute of Medicine. Field MJ, Lawrence RL, Zwanziger L, editors. Extending Medicare coverage for preventive and other services. Washington, DC: National Academies Press; 2000.

5. Testimony before the Subcommittee on Health, Committee on Energy and Commerce, House of Representatives. Washington, DC: United States Government Accountability Office; 2004 Sept 21.

6. Centers for Medicare and Medicaid Services. The guide to Medicare preventive services: for physicians, providers, suppliers, and others healthcare professionals. 2nd ed. 2005. [cited 2007 Aug 22]. Available from: http://www.cms.hhs.gov/MLNProducts/downloads/mps_guide_web-061305.pdf.

7. Simons-Morton B, Greene W, Gottlieb N. Introduction to health education and health promotion. 2nd ed. Long Grove (IL): Waveland Press; 1995.

8. Seabury J; Harvard School of Public Health. Tools and strategies to increase colorectal cancer screening rates: a practical guide for health insurance plans, 2005. [cited 2007 Aug 27]. Available from: http://www.hsph.harvard.edu/cancer/cancers/colon/resources/crc_insuranceguide/CRC_Manual.pdf.

9. Seabury J; Harvard School of Public Health. Tools and strategies to increase colorectal cancer screening rates: a practical guide for health insurance plans, 2005. [cited 2007 Aug 27]. Available from: http://www.hsph.harvard.edu/cancer/cancers/colon/resources/crc_insuranceguide/CRC_Manual.pdf.

10. Botto LD, Moore CA, Khoury MJ, Erickson JD. Neural-tube defects. *New England Journal of Medicine*. 1999; 341(20): 1509-1519.

11. MRC Vitamin Study Research Group. Prevention of neural tube defects: results of the Medical Research Council Vitamin Study. *Lancet*. 1991 Jul 20; 338(8760): 131-137.

12. Recommendations for the use of folic acid to reduce the number of cases of spina bifida and other neural tube defects. *MMWR* 1992 Sept 11;41 (RR-14): 1-7.

13. Food and Drug Administration. Food standards: amendment of standards of identity for enriched grain products to require addition of folic acid. *Federal Register*. 1996 Mar 5; 61: 8781-8807.

14. Berry RJ, Li Z, Erickson JD, Li S, Moore CA, Wang H, Mulinare J, Zhao P, Wong LY, Gindler J, Hong SX, Correa A. C [original] *New England Journal of Medicine*. 1999 Nov 11; 341: 1485-1490.[correction published in]. *New England Journal of Medicine*. 1999; 341(24): 1864. 1485-1490.

15. Smithells RW, Nevin NC, Seller MJ, Sheppard S, Harris R, Read AP, Fielding DW, Walker S, Schorah CJ, Wild J. Further experience of vitamin supplementation for prevention of neural tube defect recurrences. *Lancet*. 1983; 1(8332): 1027-1031.

16. Mulinare J, Cordero JF, Erickson JD, Berry RJ. Periconceptional use of multivitamins and the occurrence of neural tube defects. *Journal of the American Medical Association*. 1988 Dec 2; 260: 3141-45.

17. Oakley GP, Jr. Folic acid-preventable spina bifida and anencephaly. *Journal of the American Medical Association*. 1993 Mar 10; 269(10):1292-1293.

18. Honein MA, Paulozzi LJ, Mathews TJ, Erickson JD, Wong LY. Impact of folic acid fortification of the US food supply on the occurrence of neural tube defects. *Journal of the American Medical Association*. 2001; 285(23):2981-2986.

19. Yang Q, Botto LD, Erickson JD, Berry RJ, Sambell C, Johansen H, Friedman JM. Improvement in stroke mortality in Canada and the United States, 1990 to 2002. *Circulation*. 2006; 113: 1335-43.

Chapter 8. **Seeing the Big Picture:**
Using Epidemiology and Data
to Advance Public Health Policy

Introduction

$\mathcal{T}$wo hundred guests at a wedding end up in the emergency room with vomiting and fever. A small community near a manufacturing facility experiences an unusually high incidence of a rare cancer. A contagious virus spreads like wildfire to passengers and staff on a cruise ship. ● While these kinds of stories make good headlines, they are the life work of epidemiologists, who are often referred to as the detectives of the public health field.

●
While these kinds of stories make good headlines, they are the life work of epidemiologists, who are often referred to as the detectives of the public health field.

Epidemiology is the scientific method used to investigate, analyze, and prevent or control a population health problem. The population in question might be the entire world or a small community. In contrast to the field of medicine, which focuses on treatment for individual patients, epidemiology is the study of the distribution of disease, illness, and disability within populations, as well as the factors that influence it. If a person were to become ill from food poisoning, a doctor would offer examination and treatment. An epidemiologist would broaden the analysis to consider what food might have made the person ill, where the food came from, what tainted it, who else might be affected, and how to notify other individuals at risk.

In short, epidemiologists are interested in the problem of health, broadly defined. Their interest extends far beyond well-known infectious diseases, such as HIV/AIDS. Indeed, the concept of an epidemic is simply a health problem that exists in a community to a greater degree than one would expect.

Epidemiology is a field whose output has enormous, interdisciplinary applications,[1] including guiding decisions related to the development, implementation, and evaluation of policy. Epidemiologic methods and techniques play a critical role in health policy. This is because health policy unfolds through a constant cycle of analysis that entails examining large volumes of data, assessing positions, and formulating and evaluating options for reform. Population data analysis often functions as a core aspect of policy analysis. The same is true in healthcare policy because population data is critically important in identifying the existence or extent of a particular problem or the possible effects of different policy interventions.[2]

Epidemiologists lend much expertise to the policy analysis and formulation process. They help design the evidence-based protocols that healthcare providers use in treating patients, as well as decisions regarding the allocation of healthcare resources.[3-5]   ●   Epidemiologists also assess the latest scientific and therapeutic advances and measure the value of public and private investments to determine whether policy interventions have achieved desired outcomes.[6] These assessments are critical in shaping a wide array of policies, from immunization[7] to workplace exposure to environmental threats.

To advance evidence-based health services research, Congress established the Agency for Health Care Policy and Research in 1989.[8] In 1999 the agency was reauthorized and became The Agency for Healthcare Research and Quality (AHRQ).[9] AHRQ is an agency within the U.S. Department of Health and Human Services and is focused on the process, structure, and outcomes of healthcare and policy implications. AHRQ houses research centers that specialize in major areas of health services research, such as quality improvement and patient safety, outcomes and effectiveness of care, primary and preventive health services, and healthcare costs and sources of payment. The agency also finances and provides technical assistance related to health services research. Finally, AHRQ functions as the federal government's repository for what does and does not work in healthcare. As such, it is a chief translator of knowledge into policy and practice.[10]

●

Epidemiologists also assess the latest scientific and therapeutic advances and measure the value of public and private investments to determine whether policy interventions have achieved desired outcomes.

AHRQ has become an important voice for patient safety, supporting evaluations of best practices and strategies to prevent adverse events and medical errors. Many hospitals now use its patient safety indicators, and its road map of evidence-based best practices is used by the National Quality Forum, a major public-private partnership to promote healthcare quality.[11] AHRQ commissions extensive studies to review the scientific literature on improvements in patient safety and then translates key findings into practical tools and strategies.[12] ● AHRQ's work, along with that of others, has had a significant impact on hospitals' patient safety practices as well as reporting practices. Performance standards for hospitals have been developed, error reporting has increased, information technology has been integrated, and safety systems have been improved. AHRQ has also helped lead the development of a national policy related to quality measurement and reporting.[13]

● AHRQ's work, along with that of others, has had a significant impact on hospitals' patient safety practices as well as reporting practices.

AHRQ is led by Carolyn Clancy, MD, who has served as its director since 2003. Her story examines efforts to bring evidence-based analysis to national healthcare policy. At the local level, the story of Dale Morse, MD, MS, focuses on his investigation of measles outbreaks in his own state, which ultimately led to new vaccination guidelines for the country. Both stories show the important role of using data to drive effective responses to diseases that threaten the U.S. population. Data thus serves as the basis for guiding clinical care. ✹

National Case Study

Carolyn Clancy and the Agency for Healthcare Research and Quality

Carolyn Clancy, MD

Carolyn Clancy, MD, joined the Agency for Healthcare Research and Quality (AHRQ) in 1990 from the Medical College of Virginia in Richmond. As part of her academic duties in internal medicine, she supervised a large city clinic for six years and confronted questions about the quality of care on a daily basis. In moving to AHRQ, Clancy decided that she wanted to sit on the other side of the desk for two years before returning to academic medicine, but as she smilingly points out, sometimes the best career planning does not pan out.

The power of AHRQ comes from its independence. Founded near the end of the Reagan administration after years of discussion about the role of government in healthcare quality, AHRQ exists separately from Medicaid and Medicare, the federal government's two largest healthcare programs. In creating the agency, policymakers concluded that advancing healthcare quality should be maintained independently from cost controls.[14]   ●   Policymakers concluded that a truly independent and impartial agency could better accumulate scientific data from multiple stakeholders and then transmit findings back to those stakeholders. In turn, the stakeholders would rely on this impartial evidence to change practices.

Clancy sees her role at AHRQ as one of constant vigilance, information dissemination, and the improvement of the overall health of the U.S. population. She encourages her colleagues at the agency to continually ask, "What are the weakest links in patient treatment and safety? Which interventions work best to improve the situation, and are these interventions safe over the long term?"

●

Policymakers concluded that a truly independent and impartial agency could better accumulate scientific data from multiple stakeholders and then transmit findings back to those stakeholders.

The process for developing practice recommendations has evolved gradually at AHRQ. Initially, the agency created multidisciplinary advisory committees comprising practitioners, experts, and professional organizations — all of whom weighed relevant and reliable evidence before reaching a consensus. Frequently, the mix included epidemiologists who contributed cost-benefit analyses and examined scientific data. In 1996, the agency stepped back from direct involvement with guidelines development, recognizing that many professional organizations were developing their own and that the agency's essential contribution was to bring rigorous evidence to the process.

At the same time, the agency launched the National Guidelines Clearinghouse (NGC), an Internet-based repository of evidence-based guidelines with clear inclusion and updating criteria.

●   Shifting the focus to strong science rather than to expert opinion brought substantial credibility to the concept of evidence-based best practices. Indeed, government agencies, hospitals, and clinicians around the world have come to rely on them. Clancy reports that AHRQ has been gratified to discover that the NGC site attracts steadily increasing traffic from the U.S. as well as from overseas.

> Shifting the focus to strong science rather than to expert opinion brought substantial credibility to the concept of evidence-based best practices.

An example of how AHRQ's focus has evolved is its guidelines for treating high blood pressure, a recurring healthcare problem. Clancy says, "Because our panels were multidisciplinary, they made the guidelines really long. It was very hard to write a focused guideline. At the end, we produced a short multidisciplinary textbook that had not existed for many conditions such as high blood pressure. But this type of effort still is removed from what an organization needs to do to transform care." In fact, many organizations experienced major challenges when it came to developing strategies to implement practice improvements. She adds, "For high blood pressure, one of the most important things to do is to make sure that patients return regularly. Figuring out how to make sure that happens, no matter who is on shift, is what you have to do, and no guideline can tell you how to do that. That is a local phenomenon."

Practice guidelines can be controversial, particularly when they challenge conventional wisdom or limit professional autonomy. Not surprisingly, ● AHRQ encountered pressure over its practice guidelines, as medical and health professionals challenged protocols that were in contrast to their own custom and practice style. In response to this resistance, AHRQ shifted toward a greater emphasis on the underlying methodologies by which the evidence for the guidelines is produced. Clancy notes, "The truth is that we were already thinking internally about how to define the program in a way that would focus it more on our key strength, which is the methodology. The methods were key to ensuring robust evidence."

This reframing of AHRQ's approach to developing an evidence base for healthcare allowed the agency to broaden its efforts beyond clinical consensus and to begin to position the agency toward a broader evidence base, including the results of controlled trials and research. This shift also gave AHRQ a firm base with its stakeholders, including the American Medical Association and the American Association of Health Plans, which initially co-sponsored the NGC. Because guidelines now offer multiple views on the same topic along with extensive evidentiary reviews, they have become an enormous success. For example, a cardiologist may consult selected guidelines when treating a particularly severe form of heart disease, and a primary care physician may use other guidelines for more basic treatment purposes.

Following their posting, AHRQ keeps the guidelines current. For example, when the controversy surrounding the anti-inflammatory drug Vioxx arose, the guidelines mentioning the drug were immediately removed from the site. They were quickly modified to reflect the latest scientific data about safe, effective treatment with this class of drugs.

●

AHRQ encountered pressure over its practice guidelines, as medical and health professionals challenged protocols that were in contrast to their own custom and practice style.

The growing acceptance of evidence-based medicine in clinical practices and hospitals has supported AHRQ's mission and has enabled it to extend its reach to racial, ethnic, and socioeconomic disparities in healthcare. Clancy says, "Never before had we the capacity to see how we were doing for specific groups of patients at known risk for disparities in care."

AHRQ's focus on Medicare-financed care has allowed in-depth research because of the universality and relative consistency of the coverage. Medicare studies yield results that transcend populations and settings. The ability to accurately compare treatments with evidence-based standards has permitted policymakers to see the gaps between what should be done and what actually happens. Clancy notes the impact of these studies on current public and private sector efforts to realign payments with healthcare quality standards. Under her leadership, AHRQ has taken initial steps in that direction by establishing the National Quality Measures Clearinghouse.

Medicare data also make subpopulation studies possible, particularly studies that examine racial, ethnic, and socioeconomic disparities, as well as disparities by site of care. The Medicare studies underscore the relationship between large differences in treatment patterns and disproportionately worse clinical outcomes among low-income and minority patients. In other words, the research methods of epidemiology — statistical power and the use of robust data sources — make visible what previously was only suspected. Clancy says, ● "We have identified the existence of a huge gap between the best possible care and the care that people receive. In general, these gaps tend to be larger still for people who are poor or members of racial and ethnic minority populations."

●
"We have identified the existence of a huge gap between the best possible care and the care that people receive."

An additional change during Clancy's leadership has been the advent of the Consumer Assessment of Healthcare Providers and Systems (CAHPS). This special patient survey applies quantitative analytic techniques to transform individual patient experiences into evidence on the relationship between patient populations and the healthcare system. CAHPS has enabled AHRQ, policymakers, and health system stakeholders to understand how the healthcare system addresses the needs of various patient subgroups through evidence of the quality of care as seen from the patient's perspective.

● From a public policy standpoint, AHRQ's efforts have helped bring about a sea change in U.S. medical practice, shifting the focus from highly decentralized and individualized practice toward a population emphasis rooted in systematically gathered evidence and supplemented by clinical consensus and patient experience. This has led to a fundamental rethinking about the role of financing in healthcare and a greater emphasis on payment methods that advance evidence-based practice. ❈

●

From a public policy standpoint, AHRQ's efforts have helped bring about a sea change in U.S. medical practice.

Local Case Study

Dale Morse and the
New York State Measles Outbreaks

Dale Morse, MD, MS

*I*n May 1982, two counties in New York State, Dutchess and Ulster, experienced outbreaks of measles in school children. Dale Morse, MD, MS, who had joined the New York State Department of Health (NYSDOH) in Albany two years earlier as director of the Bureau of Communicable Disease Control, led a multidisciplinary team in investigating the outbreaks. The team was perplexed because its exhaustive search of school health records proved that the population was well-immunized. Who were these students? When had they been vaccinated? Which vaccine lot had been used? The NYSDOH team, together with local health authorities in Dutchess and Ulster counties, faced the prospect of daunting detective work.

An extensive epidemiologic investigation showed no association with the healthcare providers who administered the vaccine, the vaccine used, or the technique of administration. When analyzed separately, the team could only find three variables associated with an increased risk of developing disease: the number of immunizations received, the age in months at the time of immunization, and the interval since last immunization. Unfortunately, a multivariate analysis was inconclusive because of the close interaction among the three variables and confounding of the number of doses with the other two variables. No specific cause was found, and the outbreaks resolved naturally.

The AIDS epidemic pushed measles to the back burner, although it continued to simmer around the U.S. When it resurfaced in New York in the late 1980s, Morse and his team, working closely with the Centers for Disease Control and Prevention (CDC) and its Advisory Committee on Immunization Practices (ACIP), tracked data to determine whether a second dose of measles vaccine was warranted in order to control the disease. This protocol — adding a second dose to the routine measles vaccine schedule — eventually became the accepted national standard in 1989, with recommended administration at the ages of 15 months and between four and six years.

The story of the measles outbreaks in New York highlight how data and epidemiology go hand in hand in shaping policy and how advances in public health take place when visionary leaders exert themselves. The story also demonstrates how public health policy can take root at the local level before growing into national policy. Morse is quick to point out that the New York State commissioner of health at that time, Dr. David Axelrod, led the way. He says, "This policy is about multiple players and a commissioner clearly involved. He was the champion, leading this in terms of making the final policy decision."

What brought Morse to NYSDOH? A native of upstate New York who was always interested in numbers, he grew up on a farm and majored in biology as a student at Cornell University. Summer jobs on the Navajo Indian Reservation and at the Monroe County Department of Health in Rochester awakened his interest in public health and cutting-edge epidemiology. These summer experiences led him to become an Epidemic Intelligence Service (EIS) officer at the CDC after he had graduated from and completed an internship at the University of Rochester School of Medicine. He says, ● "I suddenly realized that they would actually pay you to conduct outbreak investigations and have these types of adventures!" In two years, he traveled throughout the country on 23 trips to investigate 13 epidemics, resulting in 12 publications. He then completed his residency in internal medicine before joining the NYSDOH.

●

"I suddenly realized that they would actually pay you to conduct outbreak investigations and have these types of adventures!"

During the 1970s, the CDC actively sought to eliminate measles, leading to ACIP's 1978 announced goal of eliminating the disease from the United States by Oct. 1, 1982. After conducting extensive studies, ACIP concluded that a single dose of measles vaccine administered to children between the ages of 12 and 15 months should become the recommended national policy. This single-dose policy was predicted to provide immunity to 95 percent of the immunized population, and was thought to be sufficient to confer "herd immunity" over time and contain outbreaks. However, the outbreaks in New York and elsewhere raised legitimate questions about whether this approach could contain the disease in the population. Since the United States welcomed a constant influx of people from countries where immunization standards were either different or nonexistent, the threat of measles would likely grow if the single-dose schedule were to remain in place.

In fact, measles outbreaks continued in New York and in other states throughout the 1980s. In 1987, the NYSDOH became particularly concerned with a months-long outbreak at Dartmouth College in New Hampshire. As Dartmouth athletes traveled to New York to compete against college teams in the state, Axelrod sent a letter to Dartmouth's president and to the presidents at all the New York colleges who competed against them, requesting that athletic contests be canceled.

● When Dartmouth was not cooperative, Axelrod took the unusual step of asking the state police to meet a bus of Dartmouth athletes at the state border and to turn it back. Shortly afterward, Axelrod prohibited Cornell, Columbia, and Syracuse universities from competing at the Eastern Sprint Rowing Championships in Worcester, Mass., if Dartmouth participated. In response, Dartmouth voluntarily withdrew its team. After these incidents, compliance with Axelrod's request improved dramatically.

Two years later in 1989, more than 18,000 cases of measles were reported in the United States, representing a greater than fivefold increase from the year before. Within New York, new measles outbreaks involved 21 colleges and high schools, including Siena College in Albany, whose basketball team was nearing the end

● When Dartmouth was not cooperative, Axelrod took the unusual step of asking the state police to meet a bus of Dartmouth athletes at the state border and to turn it back.

of a season that promised a rare NCAA tournament appearance. The NYSDOH allowed Siena to play the remainder of its games, provided that the team played in empty arenas and players on both sides proved they had received a second dose of vaccine or had serologic evidence of immunity to measles.   ●   In a matter of months, 21 colleges and high schools yielded 91 cases of measles, and 53,000 doses of vaccine were administered at a cost of $859,000 for the vaccine alone.

Axelrod expressed, in the strongest terms, his desire to end the outbreaks once and for all — regardless of the cost and regardless of ACIP protocol. Morse and his team reviewed the new 1989 outbreak data, which showed that most of the individuals with measles had been immunized with only one dose of vaccine. Morse's team concluded that a second dose of vaccine was needed in order to prevent ongoing outbreaks in school and college populations. Axelrod convened an advisory panel of credible experts, including representatives from the CDC, to explore how best to proceed. In April 1989, the panel adopted a recommendation for a measles two-dose policy, which was in direct conflict with ACIP's one-dose position.[16] At that time, however, the federal government was unwilling to cover the costs of the additional vaccine. New York acted alone and made the vaccine available wherever it was indicated within the state. Adamant, Axelrod insisted that the outbreaks be controlled no matter what the costs. He used the panel's findings to convince the New York Legislature that laws were needed to enforce that second dose of measles vaccine.

The movement from recognizing that a second dose of measles vaccine was needed to actual compliance took more time. In June 1989, the New York Legislature enacted a law that required that all entering kindergarten students and first-time college students in the state show evidence that they had received a second dose of measles vaccine before attending classes. This new requirement did not take effect until August 1990; this allowed time for people to be immunized. College upper classmen were also required

●

In a matter of months, 21 colleges and high schools yielded 91 cases of measles, and 53,000 doses of vaccine were administered at a cost of $859,000 for the vaccine alone.

to show evidence of the second dose, but they had a longer period (until August 1991) in which to comply. Despite this seemingly long lead time, Morse says, "New York State was relatively quick in converting a health policy into a legislative requirement."

At the same time that New York was tackling its stubborn 1989 measles outbreaks, ACIP began revisiting its protocol for measles vaccine, using the evidence amassed by Morse's multidisciplinary team and other researchers. Multiple studies concluded that a single dose of the measles vaccine was insufficient to provide herd immunity and to control outbreaks. ● Also, New York's aggressive policy of administering second doses to affected populations proved effective in stemming outbreaks. In December 1989, eight months after New York's decision and after 10 years of debate on the issue, ACIP published its own recommendation for a two-dose schedule for the MMR vaccine (comprising measles, mumps, and rubella), which came with federal assistance for meeting the costs of the vaccine. ACIP's advisory coincided with the legislation passed in New York mandating the two-dose schedule.

● Also, New York's aggressive policy of administering second doses to affected populations proved effective in stemming outbreaks.

Published peer-reviewed papers and presentations at national meetings, along with New York's strong actions, proved to be major factors in convincing the New York Legislature to act and then ACIP to recommend the two-dose schedule for the measles vaccine. If anything, Morse wishes his team had acted more swiftly in conveying to the public the outcomes of its investigations. When these outbreaks and public health responses were picked up by the press, they gained much more clout, with the press usually telling the story from the patient's point of view. In seeking maximum impact for a change in policy, Morse and his team found that they needed to humanize the scientific data in order to win converts.

New York benefited from a visionary leader, David Axelrod, who valued prevention above all. Outbreaks of measles, if not immediately contained by the NYSDOH, would have cost much more in unforeseen expenses as well as in staff time. The close working relationship that Morse's investigation team forged with the CDC and ACIP was balanced by New York's willingness to act alone.   ●   The process of pulling together while pushing apart gave rise to a national policy of the two-dose schedule for the measles vaccine. ✾

●

The process of pulling together while pushing apart gave rise to a national policy of the two-dose schedule for the measles vaccine.

Lessons Learned

*C*lancy's and Morse's leadership shows through in their emphasis
on the public good. Clancy believes that the United States is going
through a period of great change in which the public good is
gradually surfacing as the key goal of government policy. When
government discovers that it lacks the resources by itself to
deliver needed reforms — very much her experience at AHRQ —
it may turn to public-private partnerships to find the necessary
resources to solve problems. Yet in the end, the goal is still the
public good. Every guideline published by AHRQ represents just
such public-private partnerships. Every quality measure to come
also will depend on those partnerships. Clancy views leadership as
an exciting process of communicating about very specific topics,
analyzing how they relate to each other, and connecting all the
dots internally.   ●   She says, "There is nothing like positive
incentive, because at the end of the day, people would really go
the extra mile if they think what they are doing is important."

●

[Clancy] says,
"There is
nothing like
positive incentive,
because at the
end of the day,
people would
really go the extra
mile if they think
what they are
doing is
important."

Morse, perhaps somewhat ironically, became a member of ACIP
in 2005 and was recently named its chair. He likes to quote
Dwight Eisenhower and Theodore Roosevelt on leadership.
Eisenhower said, "Leadership is the art of getting someone else
to do something you want done because he wants to do it."
Roosevelt said, "The best executive is the one who has sense
enough to pick good men to do what he wants done and
self-restraint to keep from meddling with them while they do it."
According to Morse, one of today's greatest challenges in public
health is the looming population of aging baby boomers and
their associated public health problems of chronic diseases,
healthcare needs, and workplace replacement issues. He belongs
to that generation and, therefore, has a personal stake in the
leadership challenges ahead.

What do Clancy's and Morse's stories demonstrate about public health policy and leadership?

The Role of Public Health in Policy

The AHRQ and New York stories illustrate how to create a public health policy context for understanding population health problems. They also illustrate how leadership techniques can transform medicine itself, allowing healthcare professionals to see the impact of practice styles on populations, as well as the value of evidence-based interventions that alter existing approaches to clinical practice. The advent of epidemiology in medicine, championed by Clancy, helps create a solid foundation that allows medical care to rest on facts, rather than on anecdotes.

The story of Morse and his investigations of measles outbreaks in New York show how data and epidemiology can go hand in hand in shaping policy. Furthermore, his story demonstrates how a local public health policy can grow into national policy if the evidence is presented.

Sound Policy Analysis in Public Health Practice

Data collection is one of the most powerful drivers of healthcare reform, and epidemiologists are critical to this process.
● Using epidemiological data to impact the practice of medicine is changing not only clinical practice but also how policymakers think about medical care.

The tools put into use by AHRQ under Clancy's leadership have created a strong evidence base for new standards of care, which in turn, should ensure advances in population health. In addition, there is growing acceptance of evidence-based medicine in clinical practices and hospitals, which has enabled AHRQ to extend its research to disparities in healthcare.

Morse's careful analysis of measles outbreaks provided evidence that existing clinical guidelines were insufficient to protect the

● Using epidemiological data to impact the practice of medicine is changing not only clinical practice but also how policy-makers think about medical care.

population from the disease. Going against established clinical recommendations, Morse and his team proposed new guidelines that were based on his data analyses. ● His work, which was fortunately supported by a forward-thinking health commissioner, saved his state and possibly the nation from future epidemics.

The Role of Individuals

The stories of Clancy and Morse prove that leaders need to be flexible in the face of resistance. Convincing entrenched stakeholders to change can be challenging. Clancy sees her role at AHRQ as one of constant vigilance, information dissemination, and improvement of the overall health of the U.S. population. Her story illustrates how leaders who confront strong resistance can identify alternate pathways to change that help stakeholders and policymakers accept practice guidelines that are built on systematic evidence.

Morse and his team realized that by humanizing the scientific data they collected, they could more quickly convince stakeholders and policymakers to change. Local media coverage of the measles outbreaks, told from the patient's point of view, was critical in educating the public about the need for action. In this case, individual patient stories had a transformative impact on the population's health.

Advocacy for Public Health Policy

Communication and translation of evidence into the language of health policy are critical to policy change. When public health professionals are viewed as simply challenging conventional wisdom using obscure research techniques, one can expect high resistance to their findings. But when they broaden their focus to include communication and outreach to stakeholders and policymakers, the results can be dramatic.

●

[Morse's] work, which was fortunately supported by a forward-thinking health commissioner, saved his state and possibly the nation from future epidemics.

When combined with communications efforts, population research can have tangible results. ● Achieving policy change means not only carefully approaching a particular population problem but also framing and explaining the problem so that broader policy audiences can hear what is being said and feel involved in the solution. Clancy and AHRQ continue to achieve this through evidence-based guidelines, which are shared publicly. Morse and the NYSDOH communicated their findings directly to the population most at risk — schools and universities — as well as to the public in order to create change.

The examples of Clancy and Morse demonstrate how the application of surveillance and health outcomes data, using sound epidemiology principles, is essential to establishing standards and policies in public health and clinical care. But it is their translational abilities — from patient to community to state to federal — that make them public health policy leaders. They have learned how to make data come alive and in turn motivate policymakers to take action. ❋ ❋

●

Achieving policy change means not only carefully approaching a particular population problem but also framing and explaining the problem.

References

1. Friis FH, Sellers TA. Epidemiology for public health practice. 3rd ed. Jones and Bartlett Publishers: Sudbury; 2004.

2. Friis FH, Sellers TA. Epidemiology for public health practice. 3rd ed. Jones and Bartlett Publishers: Sudbury; 2004.

3. Agency for Healthcare Research and Quality [Home page on the Internet]. Rockville: Health information exchange policy issues. [cited 2007 Apr 18]. Available from:
http://healthit.ahrq.gov/portal/server.pt?open=514&objID=5554&mode=2&holderDisplayURL=http://prodportallb.ahrq.gov:7087/publishedcontent/publish/communities/k_o/knowledge_library/key_topics/health_briefing_04052006112504/health_information_exchange_policy_issues.html.

4. Agency for Healthcare Research and Quality [Home page on the Internet]. Rockville: Health information exchange policy issues. [cited 2007 Apr 18]. Available from:
http://healthit.ahrq.gov/portal/server.pt?open=514&objID=5554&mode=2&holderDisplayURL=http://prodportallb.ahrq.gov:7087/publishedcontent/publish/communities/k_o/knowledge_library/key_topics/health_briefing_04052006112504/health_information_exchange_policy_issues.html.

5. Agency for Healthcare Research and Quality [Home page on the Internet]. Rockville: AHRQ national resource center for health information technology FAQs. [cited 2007 Apr 18]. Available from:
http://healthit.ahrq.gov/portal/server.pt?open=512&objID=656&parentname=CommunityPage&parentid=20&mode=2&in_hi_userid=3882&cached=true#faq1.

6. Fielding JE, Briss PA. Promoting evidence-based public health policy: can we have better evidence and more action? *Health Affairs*. 2006 July/Aug; 25 (4): 969-978.

7. Friis FH, Sellers TA. Epidemiology for public health practice. 3rd ed. Jones and Bartlett Publishers: Sudbury; 2004.

8. Agency for Healthcare Research and Quality [Home page on the Internet]. Rockville: Health information exchange policy issues. [cited 2007 Apr 18]. Available from: http://www.ahrq.gov/about/profile.htm.

9. Agency for Healthcare Research and Quality [Home page on the Internet]. Rockville: Health information exchange policy issues. [cited 2007 Apr 18]. Available from: http://www.ahrq.gov/about/profile.htm.

10. Agency for Healthcare Research and Quality [Home page on the Internet]. Rockville: What is AHRQ? [cited 2007 Aug 10]. Available from: http://www.ahrq.gov/about/whatis.htm.

11. Leape LL, Berwick DM. Five years after To Err Is Human: What Have We Learned? *Journal of the American Medical Association*, 2005 May; 293 (19): 2384-2390.

12. Agency for Healthcare Research and Quality. [Home page on the Internet]. Rockville: AHRQ profile: advancing excellence in healthcare. [cited 2007 Apr 18]. Available from: http://www.ahrq.gov/about/profile.htm.

13. Bleich S; The Commonwealth Fund. Medical errors: five years after the IOM report. 2005 July [cited 2007 Apr 18]; Publication 830. Available from: http://www.cmwf.org/usr_doc/830_Bleich_errors.pdf.

14. Gray BH. The legislative battle over health services research. *Health Affairs*, 1992 winter; 11(4): 38-66.

Chapter 9.   **A Delicate Balance:**

The Role of Public Health Law in Protecting Individuals' Rights While Safeguarding the Public's Health

Introduction

*E*veryone is familiar with the image of the scales of justice, held aloft by a blindfolded figure. The legal community must constantly find the delicate balance between an individual's freedoms and the limitations of the law. From a public health perspective, the stakes are even higher because lives can literally be at risk. Legislators wrangling with public health policy quickly find themselves trying to balance two fundamental priorities: individuals' rights to privacy, liberty, and the disposition of their property; and the government's responsibility to protect their health. Both the United States Constitution and state constitutions accord government broad powers to protect the public's health and to provide a safety net for individuals. At the same time, federal and state constitutions prohibit governments from peering into medical records; detaining them without due process, for example, under quarantine; and using citizens' property, such as for an emergency medical clinic, without their express consent.

The more that state and federal agencies know about individuals' health, the more accurately they will be able to track public health issues. However, peering into the private health information of individual citizens is limited by law. At the core of virtually all public health policy and practice lies the pivotal task of balancing governmental powers to protect the public's health with individuals' rights to privacy.

180

Chapter 9. **The Role of Public Health Law in Protecting Individuals' Rights While Safeguarding the Public's Health** · Introduction

This chapter focuses on individuals whose leadership can be seen in their enormous contributions to shaping the legal framework for public health practice and policy. Professor Lawrence Gostin has made seminal contributions both nationally and internationally to this balancing effort. Together, Barry Zuckerman, MD, and Ellen Lawton, JD, have demonstrated the critical link between legal protection for individuals and community-oriented health-care through their special legal program for children and families housed at Boston Medical Center. ❀

Chapter 9. **The Role of Public Health Law in Protecting Individuals'**
Rights While Safeguarding the Public's Health · National Case Study

181

National Case Study

Lawrence Gostin and the
Model State Emergency Health Powers Act

Lawrence Gostin, JD

*L*awrence Gostin, JD, is the associate dean of the Georgetown University Law Center and director of the Center for Law and the Public's Health, a joint undertaking of the Law Center and Johns Hopkins Bloomberg School of Public Health. Gostin defines public health law as "the study of the legal powers and duties of the state to assure that the conditions for people to be healthy and the limitations on the power of the state to constrain the autonomy, privacy, liberty, proprietary, or other legal protected interests of individuals for the protection or promotion of community health."[1] For more than 30 years, Gostin has led the effort to ensure that the legal structure that supports public health practice safeguards the health, welfare, and values of its citizens while respecting the rights of individuals.

Educated at Duke University Law School, Gostin recalls vividly a special law school assignment that involved his being admitted to a hospital for the criminally insane in Goldsboro, N.C., under the pretense of being a rapist. That experience led to his passion for mental health. After having spent a year as a Fulbright Scholar in England, he became a leading advocate for the rights of the mentally ill in the United Kingdom. He spent the next 15 years in England, first as the legal director of the National Association for Mental Health. There, he helped write the British Mental Health Act, which modernized Britain's approach to mental illness. During his years in England, Gostin brought many civil liberties cases before the European Court of Human Rights. He then became head of the National Council for Civil Liberties, the

United Kingdom's equivalent of the American Civil Liberties Union, before joining the faculty of Oxford University. Ultimately, Gostin returned to the United States to take a position at Harvard University's School of Public Health and worked to protect the rights of people with AIDS.

Gostin's passion for mental health, his seminal work modernizing mental health protection laws in the U.K., and his civil liberties work involving HIV/AIDS patients made him uniquely qualified to lead the Centers for Disease Control and Prevention's (CDC) public health law modernization effort. He recognizes that the public may lack an appreciation for public health's focus on the entire population; many people equate public health law only with acts intended to aid the poor.

Interestingly, Gostin reports that even his own family does not always understand his work. The professor winces at narrow definitions and says, "There can't be anything more important to human well-being and happiness than the health of the population. Unfortunately, saving countless statistical lives through vaccination simply does not grab the public's attention the way a single heroic medical procedure performed by a recognizable face does." Public indifference to public health has grave funding implications. ● Less than 1 percent of all governmental health expenditures go to federal and state public health agencies.

● Less than 1 percent of all governmental health expenditures go to federal and state public health agencies.

American public health law tells the story of communicable diseases and threats to the public's health through time, with each page in history adding to the legal framework. Throughout the nation's past, public health authorities have confronted threats and epidemics and enacted numerous laws that frequently stand for generations. The last time these laws were systematically updated was in the early to mid-twentieth century. As a result, many public health statutes lag behind modern concepts of public health mission, functions, and services.

How Lagging Public Health Law Can Affect Modern Public Health Practice

▶ State surveillance laws may fall behind in describing the notifiable events for which reports to public health agencies are compulsory.

▶ Laws compelling the disclosure or exchange of personally identifiable information may not take into account modern standards related to data security and the management of personal health information.

▶ Laws that guide official conduct during publicly declared emergencies may fail to clearly spell out the circumstances under which officials will be empowered to exercise such extraordinary powers as detention, isolation, and quarantine of members of the population.

▶ Public health agency conduct that is broadly permitted in one state may be prohibited in another or limited to only certain classes of communicable diseases or threats, thereby creating enormous variation in the safety and quality of the food, air, or water supply.

A clear example of how public health law is out of date is its treatment of man-made and naturally occurring public health threats. Manufactured biological weapons and highly contagious diseases pose a risk to national security, in part, because they can be disseminated easily or transmitted from person to person, resulting in high mortality rates. Additionally, the panic and social disruption of such events would likely require special action in terms of public health preparedness.[2] Given patients' understandable demands for privacy, some states do not require public health agencies to monitor data held by hospitals, managed care organizations, and pharmacies and may even prohibit them from doing so.[3] Some statutes permit public health agencies to exercise certain powers, such as quarantine, but not others, such as directly observed therapy. State laws may permit the exercise of powers to contain certain diseases (smallpox and tuberculosis, for example) but not others, such as hemorrhagic fevers.[4] Many statutes fail to provide adequate powers to deal with the full range of health threats. Frustratingly, statutes rarely provide clear standards and fair procedures for agencies authorized to coerce people or institutions.[5]

In 1998, the Institute of Medicine issued a report warning about the deterioration of the public health infrastructure and weak public health legislation. The report called upon states to refresh their public health legal authorities. It was not until 2000, however, that governments and foundations launched several independent initiatives to take the first concrete steps toward public health legal preparedness. These initiatives included the Turning Point Public Health Statute Modernization Collaborative, funded by the Robert Wood Johnson Foundation, and the Public Health Law Program at the CDC. Another initiative was the Gilmore Commission, an advisory panel chartered by Congress to assess the capabilities of domestic response to terrorism involving weapons of mass destruction. In 2000, the Gilmore Commission called for public health laws to be updated as a means of dealing with potential terrorist attacks.[6]

The steps begun in 2000 held little political interest until the catastrophic events of Sept. 11, 2001. The subsequent anthrax attacks brought a new urgency to the problem of public health law.[7] The threats to health that followed — in particular, from anthrax — generated nearly unprecedented attention to the state of U.S. public health law.[8] ●   Propelled by a climate of fear, policymakers concluded that the public health legal infrastructure was inadequate; nonetheless, they were uncertain about the role of government in protecting public health from modern threats.[9] Within weeks after Sept. 11, the CDC commissioned the Center for Law and the Public's Health (the Center) to draft the Model

> Propelled by a climate of fear, policymakers concluded that the public health legal infrastructure was inadequate; nonetheless, they were uncertain about the role of government in protecting public health from modern threats.
>
>

State Emergency Health Powers Act. Housed at Georgetown and Johns Hopkins universities, the Center has a stated goal of "promoting the development and implementation of an effective public health law infrastructure."[10]

When the general counsel of the CDC approached Gostin to direct the effort, he was initially reluctant because he was about to return to Oxford as a visiting professor, and he knew that the project would require him to put his life on hold. Ultimately, realizing the gravity of the situation, he and the other Center staff undertook the assignment, virtually halting all other work while they drafted the model law. Developing the report was only the beginning of the challenge. The staff also had to sell policymakers on the concept and meet with governors, state legislators, and members of Congress as well as with key stakeholder groups, such as the American Public Health Association, the Association of State and Territorial Health Officials, and the Council of State and Territorial Epidemiologists. Gostin underscores a seminal lesson from this experience:

● The political challenges inherent in changing laws are no less, and often much greater than, the technical ones.

> The political challenges inherent in changing laws are no less, and often much greater than, the technical ones.

Moving quickly, the commission published the first draft of the model legislation on Oct. 23, 2001. The draft Model State Emergency Health Powers Act emphasized giving public health agencies sufficient and clear authority to mount adequate preparations, obtain information, and act promptly in a public health emergency. The model act was explicitly predicated on the assumption that public health emergencies require a trade-off between protecting individual civil rights and ensuring effective government interventions to safeguard the public's health.[11]

In addition to commissioning the Model State Emergency Health Powers Act, the CDC initiated and funded a major program in May 2002 to strengthen anti-terrorism preparedness among state and local public health agencies, focusing on deliberate acts of terrorism, infectious disease epidemics, and other massive health threats. Provisions in the program called on grantees to improve their public health legal preparedness.[12] The CDC's terrorism preparedness program became the first nationwide initiative for public health legal preparedness. ● This initiative rested on the belief that in the event of a bioterrorist attack, only a well-considered and balanced legal response would ensure public safety and limit panic. Particularly important would be evidence that public health authorities had a legal basis on which to act, and acted fairly, before restricting individuals' freedoms in the name of the broader collective good.[13]

The model act needed to address a host of issues beyond those that policymakers tend to think of when they focus on public health protection law, such as quarantine, screening, testing, and medical treatment isolation. This law would need to address the obligation of pharmaceutical companies to make stockpiles of drugs and vaccines available. It would also need to address the obligations of hospitals to communicate any suspicious cases in their care and also to provide for the compensation of hospitals that were forced to become centers for quarantine or treatment. As the Constitution requires that government powers be carefully delineated, the commission relied on the Department of Justice and many other groups for help in addressing difficult legal questions. Basic questions needed answers: Under what circumstances may a governor declare a state of emergency? How should terrorism be defined? How are emerging infectious diseases defined?

Gostin and his team addressed a host of intellectual challenges in drafting the model act. Would the model consider emergencies that arise only from bioterror, or should every conceivable hazard be considered? How might approaches to chemical, nuclear, and radiation hazards differ from a public health response to biological hazards? Most challenging of all was the balance that had to be struck with individuals' rights and due process and the protection of the common good in a public health emergency.

●

This initiative rested on the belief that in the event of a bioterrorist attack, only a well-considered and balanced legal response would ensure public safety and limit panic.

Public health officials were unequivocal in supporting an approach that pared down the number of procedures and rights and maximized their authority to act decisively in an emergency.

The draft Model State Emergency Health Powers Act caused controversy over the extent to which people should cede civil liberties for the common good. As Gostin's team would attest, the intellectual challenges of drafting the model act paled in comparison with the political challenges. Committed as he had been to civil liberties over his entire working career, he says that he was aghast at the battles he now fought with civil libertarians from the extremes of the left and right. In his view, both sides ignored the commission's efforts to draft a model law that attempted to ensure appropriate public health powers while protecting individual liberties and rights. Although the model act gave strong powers to public health authorities, individual safeguards included in the act were, in Gostin's view, clearer than the current laws at the time.

The following excerpts illustrate the original sweep of the model statute and shed light on why the initial effort might have caused such consternation among civil liberties groups. These excerpts also underscore the degree of difficulty faced by the team.

▶ Governors would be explicitly empowered to declare a state of public health emergency that would give state public health officials the authority to take over all healthcare facilities (public and private), to order physicians to act in certain ways, and to order citizens to submit to examinations and treatment. People who refused would be subject to quarantine or criminal punishment.[14]

▶ Public health officials and those working under their authority would be immune from liability for their actions, including actions causing permanent injury or death; the only exceptions would be in cases of gross negligence and willful misconduct.[15]

► The declaration of a state public health emergency would permit governors to suspend state regulations, alter the functions of state agencies, and mobilize the National Guard.[16]

► Public health personnel would be given exceptionally broad powers, and criminal sanctions would be imposed on physicians and individuals who failed to follow their orders.[17]

► Any person refusing to submit to medical examination and/or testing would be guilty of a misdemeanor.[18]

Gostin and his team faced ferocious responses from lobbyists representing every conceivable group — hospitals, the pharmaceutical industry, the trucking industry and other transportation systems, the food industry, patient rights advocates, and property rights advocates. The drafting team faced opposition from three main groups: the healthcare industry resisting greater regulation, civil liberties advocates stressing individuals' rights, and individuals believing that the politics of delineating power would render the entire exercise academic. Gostin was perplexed when the American Hospital Association cheered at the idea of quarantines while advocating that hospitals not be the quarantine sites. Special-interest groups and their lobbyists can, unfortunately, be motivated by self-interest, which can work against the collective interest that lies at the heart of public health. At the same time, the media often promote controversy at the expense of consensus. As he points out, "We always have the extreme of the political spectrum debating one another, and this is not a good way for the public to understand complex public health problems."

Following the first round of criticisms, the team published a revised version in December 2001. The revision reflected the commission's effort to balance the government's interest in imposing control measures, such as quarantine, civil confinement, and mandatory treatment in fighting epidemics with individual constitutional rights to due process, freedom of movement, and bodily integrity.[19] The revised draft continued to call for circumscribing certain civil rights and freedoms in order to achieve public safety and health in the face of bioterrorism, and it continued to arouse objections from civil liberties advocates.[20]

In response, the commission continued to edit the model law in consultation with stakeholders, issuing a final model act in the spring of 2002. The effort to gain acceptance and adoption continued, as the Center staff traveled throughout the nation and met with state officials. At the same time, the staff found the public response gratifying. Gostin says, "It is really remarkable how huge a deal it was at the time. People were very focused on it, very concerned.   ●   I wish I could have gotten such political attention before for ongoing public health concerns rather than just for terrorism in an emergency context." At a meeting of state attorneys general, Gostin distributed the model act to board members and requested comments in writing. By the end of the weekend, after the board members had departed for home, virtually every state submitted comments.

> ●
> "I wish I could have gotten such political attention before for ongoing public health concerns rather than just for terrorism in an emergency context."

In defending the Model State Emergency Health Powers Act before various audiences over the course of a year, Gostin saw firsthand how individualistic American society had become. Opponents of the act, whether from the left or right, always defended individual rights: the left citing civil liberties, privacy rights, and autonomy; the right citing property rights, free enterprise, and freedom of contract. He believes that, in essence, little other than the theoretical base on which their views rest now separates the extremes on the left and right. He favors a passage from a speech by President Franklin D. Roosevelt, in which he said, "The success or failure of any government in the final analysis must be measured by the well-being of its citizens. Nothing can be more important to a state than its public health. The state's paramount concern should be the health of its people."

Despite his career fighting for individuals' rights and civil liberties, Gostin laments the fact that Roosevelt's sentiments seem far from reality in today's America. With every turn of the political wheel, individuals' rights seem to trump the collective interest.

He is hopeful, however, that the nation has begun to return to a focus on the common good. While the country's traditional laws and ethics focus on individual rights and while bioethics trumpets individual autonomy, privacy, and integrity, he detects an emerging focus on public health ethics.

The Model State Emergency Health Powers Act has been exceptionally successful, despite much controversy and a grueling process in drafting a final product. In 2003, when the SARS epidemic swept through Canada, China, and Hong Kong, those governments turned to the model act to address their own dire circumstances. By mid-2006, the model act had been adopted in full or in part by 38 states and the District of Columbia. The national press — including *The New York Times, The Washington Post,* and *USA Today* — supported its adoption. Under pressure to write something quickly, the commission members did not have time to seek input from all of the stakeholders as fully, or as early, as they might have liked. At each stage, however, opponents had opportunities to make their reservations known. Nonetheless, Gostin takes pride in his team's final result. ● He remarks, "We never expected the law to have such a practical impact that it would be enacted and influential in so many places in the country."

> ●
>
> "We never expected the law to have such a practical impact that it would be enacted and influential in so many places in the country."

The model law has, in fact, become influential in the teaching of health law and has appeared in legal casebooks, public health law casebooks, and public health readers. When the population faces a major threat, what extraordinary powers should the governor and public health agencies exercise? What are the checks and balances, and how can individual rights and civil liberties be balanced with the common good? The model law illustrates trade-offs between public health and individuals' rights.

With the success of the model act and a growing acceptance of a broader Model State Public Health Act that grew out of the original Turning Point initiative, Gostin views global health as his next big challenge. The World Health Organization (WHO) invited him to write a model global public health law based on the two model acts in the United States. In his future work, he intends to focus on widespread diseases, such as tuberculosis, HIV/AIDS, and malaria, and to find solutions to these global problems. He views leadership not only as leading by example and inspiration but also taking the path less traveled. As he observes, ● "You have to be a leader where nobody wants to be a leader."

"You have to be a leader where nobody wants to be a leader."

In strong terms, Gostin cautions public health leaders to be fully engaged in national, state, and local politics. He finds that many leaders in public health are suspicious of the political process and of politicians, and he believes that this is a big mistake. To be politically engaged does not mean having to be political, he says. He also cautions public health leaders not to assume that the public agrees with them on the primacy of public health. The public can be diverted easily by issues they perceive to be more important, such as the price of gasoline or road construction or national defense. Public health leaders must engage the political world across its full spectrum if public health is to be a lasting priority.

Gostin remembers his late colleague and close friend, Jonathan Mann, who understood public health and human rights. Mann began his global campaign against AIDS in an office at the WHO with just two people, and it grew into the largest office in the history of the WHO. An important aspect of his work, and an inspiration for Gostin, was maintaining the delicate balance between protecting the public's health and preserving human rights.

In many ways, Gostin's work traced the outline of a single ethical question in public health: whether an individual's right to privacy and freedom to make choices outweighs the government's imperative to strong action, especially in emergencies, to protect the public's health. His experiences illustrate the intricate social, political, and policy processes that underlie the law. Another approach is how existing law can be used every day to help families live in healthier and safer environments. This is the story of Barry Zuckerman and Ellen Lawton. ✲

Local Case Study

Barry Zuckerman, Ellen Lawton, and
the Medical-Legal Partnership for Children —
Raising the Bar for Child Health

While Larry Gostin focused on the creation of a broad legal framework, the focus of medical-legal partnerships is local and uses existing laws to advance health through a new model of partnership involving medical care, public health, and the law. Barry Zuckerman, MD, and Ellen Lawton, JD, colleagues at the Boston Medical Center, have combined their expertise in pediatrics and the law to create a program known as the Medical-Legal Partnership for Children — Raising the Bar for Child Health. Founded in 1992 by Zuckerman, with Lawton joining in 1998, this new approach to child and family health began as a local effort that, ultimately, grew into a national movement.

Barry Zuckerman, MD

Zuckerman has experience leading local efforts that grow into national movements. His earlier innovative effort promoting child development and literacy is known as Reach Out and Read (www.reachoutandread.org). This initiative, begun in 1988 at Boston City Hospital, today reaches 2.8 million children. It provides 4.6 million free books in more than 3,200 programs in the 50 states, the District of Columbia, Puerto Rico, and Guam. More than 46,000 pediatricians, nurses, residents, and other health professionals hand out these books during visits.

Ellen Lawton, JD

The aim of the Medical-Legal Partnership is twofold. The first is to advance community health one family at a time through the effective use of law. The second is to align individual representation with broader legislative and systemic advocacy when many families have the same problems. Simply and elegantly, the program transforms the way low-income people obtain needed legal services. By identifying legal problems that impair families from securing such basic needs as food, housing, personal safety, and access to education and healthcare, the program is designed to produce immediate improvement in children's health.

The program reflects Zuckerman's long-standing frustration, which is shared by many other health professionals, at seeing children's health improve in the hospital only to see them return to the very environments that compromised their health. He saw his patients returning to unheated and unlit homes and to unsafe neighborhoods and schools. After regaining their strength, children would revert to a diet that left them weakened by malnourishment. Children with asthma would return to homes and schools with the poor air quality that had triggered their attacks in the first place.

Poor health may also affect children's ability to succeed in school. Children with sickle cell anemia, for example, may be hospitalized for several days every month as a result of cyclical pain and may miss days in the classroom, constantly struggling to keep up with schoolwork. Many schools provide tutors only when a student misses 10 consecutive days of school, a service of no use at all to children who might need only two consecutive days in the hospital but on an ongoing, perhaps monthly, basis.

> Zuckerman could see that children's basic needs were not being met... More precisely, he realized that legal help was necessary.

Zuckerman could see that children's basic needs were not being met; furthermore, he realized that treating only the immediate health problem had limited impact. More precisely, he realized that legal help was necessary, given the complex legal environment in which society and families function. For example, while Massachusetts had among the lowest number of food stamp recipients per capita in the country, he understood that this low rate was not because of lack of need, but rather as a result of legal and bureaucratic hurdles that proved insurmountable to families who urgently required assistance. He further concluded that health professionals were doing an inadequate job of helping families overcome these barriers, focusing instead on health insurance and payment rates. He thought pediatricians would greatly enhance the health of

194

Chapter 9. **The Role of Public Health Law in Protecting Individuals' Rights While Safeguarding the Public's Health** · Local Case Study

those in their care if they could become forceful advocates for food stamps and affordable housing.

Zuckerman saw a need to create partnerships between pediatricians and lawyers who had the skill and the time to help low-income people live healthier lives. As a pediatrician, he cared most about prevention and wanted to pass that passion along to a number of lawyers. Lawyers usually see clients only after a catastrophe, such as child abuse or eviction, but Zuckerman wanted to work side by side with public health lawyers to prevent such problems and the negative impact they have on children. As social conditions and health are linked, he needed to develop a strategy that would join legal and medical services to advance the best interests of children.

●　　To improve the poor social conditions that are pervasive among low-income populations, he paired lawyers with health-care providers. For example, research demonstrated that children from families that are eligible for Section 8 public housing assistance are less likely to be hungry, malnourished, or in general poor health than children in families on the waiting list. Yet it is lawyers, not pediatricians, who know how to petition for Section 8 certificates on behalf of families whose children can then become healthier.

As chairman of the Department of Pediatrics at his hospital, Zuckerman had some leverage within his budget to start a program on a trial basis He hoped that if he was effective, financial support to sustain it would become available. Lawton defines the program that Zuckerman initiated. She says, "We're trying to change the delivery model for legal services, which historically relied on families self-diagnosing their legal problem and finding their way to the legal services office in their community. We want to be more proactive in how we help families and have them come and get screened for legal problems. Maybe we can help them before they get evicted, before they lose their jobs, before their child suffers the health impact that results from poverty."

●

To improve the poor social conditions that are pervasive among low-income populations, he paired lawyers with healthcare providers.

In the model conceived by Zuckerman and Lawton, this screening takes place just down the hall from the pediatrician's office, an important first step in helping patients receive benefits for which they qualify. Statistics show that 80 percent of poor people diagnosed with cancer fail to appear at follow-up appointments. However, when it comes to their children, even parents most at risk of losing their home or job will seek a pediatrician's help in administering vaccines and checking sore throats and ear infections. By making legal assistance available in the clinical setting, the likelihood that families will actually receive benefits increases dramatically.

Zuckerman hoped that his strategy would help the cause of legal services by placing it in an entirely new light. The legal aid community, comprising legal aid programs funded in each state by the federal government and the states, is woefully under-resourced to meet the significant need. A 1990 survey conducted by the American Bar Association concluded that the average low-income person has a minimum of three unmet legal needs. As a result, legal aid agencies traditionally practice in a reactive or "emergency room" posture. By aligning legal needs with well-child care, Zuckerman paved the way for viewing the law as a proactive tool for vulnerable populations — ensuring that parents not suffer a legal crisis, such as being evicted or fired, before receiving legal assistance. ● His brainchild, in essence, created primary care lawyers for poor people. By organizing a way for pediatricians to be paired with lawyers, he made it possible to assess both the legal and the health needs of families in one visit. The clinician's finding could be passed to a lawyer prepared to advocate for the family in order to secure a healthier future.

●

His brainchild, in essence, created primary care lawyers for poor people.

The program surmounted the steep learning curve that lawyers and doctors inevitably face when attempting to overcome their cultural differences. In doing so, they made the most of their common talents and orientation toward individual families. From case loads to patient-client communications, the two camps initially lacked the necessary common understanding needed in order to work together. For example, doctors frequently see up to 35 patients a day, and lawyers might see as few as two to three clients on a busy day. Physicians require other physicians to file reports on all referred patients; lawyers interact with each client in the strictest confidence and may devote hundreds of hours to bringing a single case to justice. It took ongoing improvement strategies over five years to develop a common approach to help implement similar programs.

Their successes have been considerable. Lawton takes particular pride in the partnership's success at countering the phenomenon she calls "heat or eat." In low-income communities during winter, heating can become such a high expense that families often skimp on food to pay fuel bills, which in turn interferes with children's growth and development. Infants who should be gaining weight steadily are at particular risk. In addition, if a family misses payments, heat in the home gets turned off. Programs exist to ameliorate this major health risk by reducing the size of payments during peak heating season. Payments can be spread uniformly over the year, and arrears in utilities payments can be managed in ways that protect children's health and save families from losing heat and electricity during winter months.

●   Through ready access to legal assistance during visits to the pediatrician, many families realized for the first time that they have a means of averting a catastrophic situation. Lawton views this achievement as evidence that the partnership's focus on advocacy has, indeed, produced the strong results that Zuckerman had hoped for.

> ●
>
> Through ready access to legal assistance during visits to the pediatrician, many families realized for the first time that they have a means of averting a catastrophic situation.

Lawton runs an advocacy boot camp — covering 10 topics in three hours for individuals who work on the front lines of immigration, housing, and public benefits — and writes manuals and other materials to help people establish new advocacy centers. She views the assistance that she offers as being minimal, however. Although favorable coverage in the national media has helped create demand, she is still amazed at the extent to which people embraced the original idea. The Center provides technical assistance to help committed pediatric and legal practices form successful partnerships.

The Medical-Legal Partnership for Children received a five-year grant worth nearly $3 million from the Kellogg and Robert Wood Johnson foundations in the fall of 2005 to help expand its reach across the country. The goal is to expand the 40 partnerships that existed at the time of the grant to 80 — with at least one in every state. As of April 2007, there were 60 partnerships in 32 states. Zuckerman continues to celebrate this grant, since his toughest partnership challenge has been to raise funds. He benefited from his experience in obtaining funding for Reach Out and Read. Federal funding for that program grew steadily from an initial $1 million, secured through Sen. Edward Kennedy and First Lady Hillary Clinton, to $10 million today, which was made possible, in part, by strong support from First Lady Laura Bush. A medical-legal partnership is far more challenging, because the idea of law raises more controversy than a reading program.

When Zuckerman first started knocking on doors at Boston's prestigious law firms, he did not envision the spiraling national success his Medical-Legal Partnership for Children would achieve.

●
The hard work of building the partnership into a national phenomenon gave meaning to his cause.

● The hard work of building the partnership into a national phenomenon gave meaning to his cause. Like every other true leader, he took delight in breaching boundaries and especially in giving accolades to people like Lawton who seized his dream and did the painstaking, meticulous work of establishing the medical-legal partnerships. The networks built by Lawton and her colleagues, as well as the well-trained advocates they produce, make it possible for countless children and families to thrive. The training and service activities set the stage for the future of medical-legal partnerships, where lawyers and pediatricians together advocate for children's basic needs beyond health insurance, and where important community partners, like private law firms, provide strategic guidance and pro bono support to promote child and family health. ❁

198

Chapter 9. **The Role of Public Health Law in Protecting Individuals' Rights While Safeguarding the Public's Health** · Lessons Learned

Lessons Learned

Gostin, Zuckerman, and Lawton represent the two dimensions of law as a public health safeguard. Gostin focuses on law and the broader public good; Zuckerman and Lawton emphasize the importance of law in protecting the health of individuals in society. This intricate balance between the laws that protect the public's health and laws that protect individuals' rights helps ensure an inclusive society that is capable of advancing the public good without sacrificing individual protections. ● For the public's health to be truly protected, a partnership must exist between an effective and strong government and individuals' civil liberties.

The following lessons learned from their examples are noteworthy:

The Role of Public Health in Policy

Gostin's work has been a testament to his favorite Roosevelt quote, which states that government has no higher calling than to protect the public's health. His achievement is in finding the right balance between individuals and populations in the modern public health legal system. His work has not been without controversy, but his policy leadership can be seen in his unflagging effort to find this balance through a highly iterative and inclusive process. He knows firsthand the degree of thoughtfulness and balance that public health law and practice require, and he has accepted the challenge of seeking this balance in an era characterized by tension and fear.

Zuckerman and Lawton represent the bookend to Gostin's work. They strive to translate a broad legal framework containing public health safeguards and protections into real gains for individual families. Their work embodies perhaps the most basic of public health truths: The health of a community reflects the health of its individual members, with the result that health gains in the

●

For the public's health to be truly protected, a partnership must exist between an effective and strong government and individuals' civil liberties.

whole population are impossible unless health improvement initiatives include tailored efforts to "lift all boats." Their innovative approach to public health breached long-held boundaries by joining legal representation with clinical medicine to produce a greater health benefit. Their idea has proved so potent within their own community that others have begun to replicate their success.

Sound Policy Analysis in Public Health Practice

Gostin's work in developing the model act revealed that existing public health laws did not conform to modern views of the mission, functions, and services of public health agencies.

● He knew that he would have to definitively make the case that public health authorities had a legal basis on which to act before restricting individuals' freedoms in the name of the broader collective good.[21] Through the wrenching process of developing the proposed law, it became clear to him that public health leaders should not assume that most people see public health as a prime government activity. Public health leaders have the additional challenge of engaging the full political spectrum to make public health a lasting priority.

> ●
> [Gostin] knew that he would have to definitively make the case that public health authorities had a legal basis on which to act before restricting individuals' freedoms in the name of the broader collective good.

For Zuckerman and Lawton, it was their understanding of the traditional roles and responsibilities of both the medical and legal communities that allowed them to create a new model of primary care lawyers. They made the connection that many health problems affecting poor families had some legal aspects to them, such as an eviction notice, the lack of proper paperwork to enroll in government assistance programs, or overdue utilities payments. All of these can lead to devastating health problems, including stress, poor nutrition, and unsafe living conditions. By having access to physicians and lawyers in the same space, patients were able to have their medical and legal needs addressed simultaneously.

The Role of Individuals

Great policy leadership is the ability to balance many interests in order to find a solution that all parties can accept. Gostin's

200

Chapter 9. **The Role of Public Health Law in Protecting Individuals' Rights While Safeguarding the Public's Health** · Lessons Learned

balancing effort required forging a middle ground between ensuring that government would have the power to act and that individuals' rights would be protected. Zuckerman and Lawton had to bridge two professional communities with mutually exclusive (and deeply held) philosophies and styles, essentially creating a third way of caring for children, families, and communities.

Importantly, these leaders have perspective on the criticisms their work originally generated. Gostin understands why his work raised such controversy and understands the need to invest enormous energy in finding a middle ground. Zuckerman and Lawton understand what it means to try to forge a new way of furnishing healthcare and the challenges that such pioneering work can raise within their professions.

Advocacy for Public Health Policy

The work of this trio also underscores that public health policy leadership is about more than vision. ● Public health policy leadership is also about dedication in the face of challenges, and transforming a singular vision into a common effort. In Gostin's case, the proof of this transformation has been the widespread adoption of the model legislation. For Zuckerman and Lawton, the proof of their success is the national growth of their integrated medical-legal model.

The stories of these three individuals illustrate the fact that leaders find ways around roadblocks. They persisted and transformed public health principles into practice. Their work on behalf of society and individuals demonstrates the accomplishments of people who believe that the public's health is one of society's imperatives. ❀ ❀

> ●
> Public health policy leadership is also about dedication in the face of challenges, and transforming a singular vision into a common effort.

Chapter 9. **The Role of Public Health Law in Protecting Individuals'**
Rights While Safeguarding the Public's Health · References

201

References

1. Gostin LO. Public health law: power, duty, restraint. Berkeley: University of California Press; 2000.

2. Centers for Disease Control and Prevention [Home page on the Internet]. Atlanta. Emergency preparedness & control. Bioterrorism agents/diseases by category [cited 2007 March 20]. Available from: http://www.bt.cdc.gov/agent/agentlist-category.asp#adef.

3. Gostin LO. Public health law in an age of terrorism: rethinking individual rights and common goods. *Health Affairs.* 2002 Nov/Dec; 21(6):79-93.

4. Gostin LO 79.

5. Gostin LO 79.

6. Moulton A, Gottfried RN, Goodman RA, Murphy AM, Rawson RD. What is public health legal preparedness? *Journal of Law, Medicine & Ethics.* 2003; 31(4); 1-12.

7. Moulton A 1.

8. Gostin LO, Koplan JP, Grad, FP. The law and the public's health: the foundation. In Goodman RA, Rothstein MA, Hoffman RE, Lopez W, Matthews GW, editors. Law in public health practice. Oxford, (U.K.:) Oxford University Press; 2003.

9. Gostin LO. Public health law in an age of terrorism: rethinking individual rights and common goods. *Health Affairs.* 2002 Nov/Dec; 21(6): 79-93.

10. The Center for Law and Public's Health at Georgetown and Johns Hopkins Universities [Home page on the Internet]. Baltimore: Our mission. [cited 2007 March 20]. Available from: http://www.publichealthlaw.net/About/Mission.htm.

11. Annans GJ. Legal issues in medicine: bioterrorism, public health, and civil liberties. *New England Journal of Medicine.* 2002 Apr 25; 346(17): 1261-1264.

12. Moulton A, Gottfried RN, Goodman RA, Murphy AM, Rawson RD 1.

13. Gostin LO. Public health law: power, duty, restraint. Berkeley: University of California Press; 2000.

14. Annans GJ. Legal issues in medicine: bioterrorism, public health, and civil liberties. *New England Journal of Medicine.* 2002 Apr 25; 346(17): 1261-1264.

15. Annans GJ 1261.

16. Annans GJ 1261.

17. Annans GJ 1261.

18. Annans GJ 1261.

19. Goodman RA, Rothstein MA, Hoffman RE, Lopez W, Mathews GW, Foster KL. Law in public health practice. Oxford, UK: Oxford University Press; 2003.

20. Gostin LO. Public health law in an age of terrorism: rethinking individual rights and common goods. *Health Affairs.* 2002 Nov/Dec; 21(6): 79.

21. Gostin LO. Public health law: power, duty, restraint. Berkeley: University of California Press; 2000

Concluding Thoughts

The profiles contained in this book illustrate the richly diverse nature of public health policy leadership. Whether the issue is building a health center in rural Mississippi, attempting to modernize the nation's system of public health laws, or using data to make the case for basic improvements in healthcare access and patient safety, the individuals profiled here share certain basic qualities.

The Quality of Vision

Leadership qualities begin with a unique type of vision — the ability to see the broader social dimensions of what otherwise might be viewed as a problem specific to certain individuals or communities. Policy leaders invariably possess a panoramic view of health. They understand that what might appear at first to be individual conduct cannot be truly understood if that conduct is disconnected from the society in which individuals live.

This gift of vision and a broader social perspective can be seen in every profile in this book. For Jack Geiger, the poor health of rural African-American families in the South did not signal a problem with their own health behavior; rather, it signaled to him a problem with the ways in which the health system as a whole behaved toward and interacted with individuals. Geiger's solution was to change the system, an advance in public health policy that, in turn, changed the health of the population.

For Rashi Fein, the lack of health insurance among the elderly was not a function of their failure to plan properly in old age; instead, it was a symptom of a far larger social problem, namely the absence of policies that made coverage possible. Similarly, for Joe Thompson, childhood obesity was not simply a one-family-at-a-time affair. Childhood obesity was, in great part, about the ways in which society interacts with children. To permit individual families to choose health for their children, Thompson understood that the state of Arkansas had to change the ways in which the pillars of society (such as the school system) interacted with children and their families, thereby creating and enabling the choice of good health.

Is it possible to acquire long-term vision, or are people born with it?
It is true that the ability to see life in its full and broad context has an
aspect of personality to it. At the same time, it is possible to learn to
see the world against which individual conduct unfolds. Indeed, the
formal policy analysis process — with its emphasis on conducting an
environmental policy scan, performing a stakeholder analysis, and
formulating options that rely on evidence-based research and population
data — is really about learning how to use the vision of policy thought
and orientation.

The Quality of Commitment

One of the patterns that emerges in these profiles is the length of time
needed to bring about broader social change. Without commitment
to change in the long-term, policy leadership cannot exist.

Established leaders, such as Julius Richmond and Rashi Fein, have
devoted their entire lives to achieving broader societal change. Younger
leaders, such as Thomas Perez, Nicole Lurie and Carolyn Clancy, have
committed their professional lives to their health policy work. In every
case, his or her commitment has endured in the face of significant
setbacks, controversy, and intense pressure to back off.

It is not easy to work for broad societal change. In any society, there
are entrenched stakeholders who favor and actively seek to preserve the
status quo. Indeed, a careful policy analysis always includes the option
of doing nothing, which is often the easiest path to take. Policy leaders
are people who have committed their time and their lives to taking
action and who have learned to value small and steady gains over a
long period of time.

The Quality of Thoughtfulness

A particularly striking aspect of any interaction with a policy leader is
the extent to which the quality of thoughtfulness comes through. Policy
leaders tend not to see the world through a single frame; instead, they
view events through multiple frames that take them outside their own
way of thinking and into the minds of others. This is not to say that

policy leaders do not possess strong beliefs, a commitment to ideals, or a desire to find a quick way out of a problem. Rather, this quality of thoughtfulness means that as policy leaders formulate analyses and options, they possess the ability to grasp how others will view their forward movement and the ability to take the views of others into account. Opponents are not enemies. They are people who see the world differently and whose world views need to be taken into account to formulate solutions.

Policy leaders are invariably well-read and consume not only information that confirms their own world view but also material that tends to show the world in a different way. This ability to view life through the eyes of others and to reformulate options and policy actions in response to other competing frameworks is what many of us might call "thinking outside the box." This is the ability to take a thoughtful, fresh approach to a policy problem that shows the world a new and, perhaps, a less polarizing way forward.

The people who are profiled are all accomplished thought leaders and outside-the-box thinkers. Barry Zuckerman and Ellen Lawton imagined a new way of making pediatricians and lawyers work together for families. Joseph Thompson made schools work differently for children. Richard Gottfried re-imagined health insurance for families. Lucian Leape re-imagined what might be done inside the healthcare system to reduce medical errors. All of these thought leaders were not merely policy innovators; they understood the environments in which they were working. Through their education, training, and learned insights, they innovated ways to reframe social and system conduct.

A Final Insight...

A final insight can be drawn from the accumulated impact of these profiles. There can be no public health without policy leadership. Public health is about the health of the population, of course, but the operative word is actually *public*. If the world were in infinite balance and if all people enjoyed an equal ability to choose health, then public health would just be about educating individuals to make the right choices and about providing incentives for healthy behavior.

But there are no level playing fields. Creating an environment in which all people can choose and achieve health requires a level of thought, vision, and commitment to goals that extends outside the self. Leaders recognize the way in which external forces in society affect the lives of individuals. And leaders aim to create balance between the two. This is what public health policy is about.

Many public health practitioners fear getting involved with the policy world. There is no question that public health practice is valuable and fulfilling when the task is to gather data, issue reports, or find solutions that modify individual behavior. However, if the nation is ever to achieve optimal population health, then the public health dialogue must include the policy dimension. To advance the health of the population, the public health system must train a work force capable of, and ready to embrace, policy leadership as an inherent and critical element of the profession. This means rethinking educational curricula and work force training. It also means a dedicated effort by the public health community to recruit the types of remarkable people whose stories are told here. ❁ ❁